WITHDRAWN

A NEWTON AMONG POETS

A Newton Among Poets

Shelley's Use of Science in Prometheus Unbound

By CARL GRABO

Associate Professor of English
University of Chicago

COOPER SQUARE PUBLISHERS, INC.
NEW YORK
1968

Originally Published 1930
Published by Cooper Square Publishers, Inc.
59 Fourth Avenue, New York, N. Y. 10003
Library of Congress Catalog Card No. 68-19138

Printed in the United States of America
by Noble Offset Printers, Inc., New York, N. Y. 10003

Affectionately Inscribed

TO

My Mother

BLANCHE CHASE GRABO

PREFACE

THE MATERIAL of this book was planned as a part of the notes to an edition of *Prometheus Unbound* now in preparation. The scientific citations proved, however, to be so extensive and the need for sketching Shelley's scientific background so evident, that its independent publication was decided upon. It was also felt that facts unusual in kind, and, to many readers of Shelley, even startling, should be separately considered and weighed; for once their full significance is grasped Shelley must thereafter be thought of in a new light. Our conception of him as poet and thinker is, by reason of these findings, greatly altered.

There is no need to review here the history of Shelley's reputation as a poet nor the slow perception of his greatness, greatness which is now generally acknowledged but usually thought to lie in his emotional and lyrical powers. That Shelley was an excellent scholar, a man well read in many fields, and that he was fundamentally intellectual rather than emotional, is not widely realized. Mary Shelley's modest contention that Shelley was as notable a philosopher as poet has been smilingly put aside as the exaggeration born of a wifely devotion. One gathers, indeed, from many commentators that Shelley was a kind of inspired idiot, producing beautiful poetry without clearly knowing what he was about. It is unlikely that beautiful poetry was ever so produced.

Mr. Whitehead, whose challenge to literary critics faces the first chapter of this book, is justified in his strictures. Criticism has ignored Shelley's interest in science or belittled it. And as a consequence large sections of *Prometheus Unbound* have remained undeciphered to this day. There has been much talk of Shelley's exquisite lyricism and very little of Shelley's hard intellectual meaning. It has, indeed, not generally been conceded that Shelley in *Prometheus* had a wholly intelligible meaning.

The content of this book is an answer to Mr. Whitehead's challenge. The study of Shelley's science has proved a revelation to me, and my findings, however inadequate and incomplete, will, I think, prove a revelation to others. The task might have been better done by one who, interested in poetry and philosophy, was also versed in the history of science. But none such has volunteered for the task.

There is, however, some justification for one not technically trained in science entering this field. In Shelley's day several of the sciences were still in their infancy. Technic and vocabulary had not yet passed beyond the comprehension of the amateur. The philosophic implications of a science, if not its technical details, could be generally grasped. It was these implications which mostly concerned Shelley, though in chemistry and electricity his knowledge may have been almost professional. Science to him was one strand of human knowledge, to be woven into a synthesis with moral philosophy and metaphysics. What he was after was what all of us are after, a unified conception of the universe.

The history of his scientific thinking keeps pace with his philosophical development. He passes, that is, from a narrow materialistic and deterministic philosophy to one which seeks to reconcile Platonism with science. The way to this reconciliation lies through Newton and those of his successors who explain matter in terms of energy and identify energy with the spirit of animation. Newton's speculations merge with Platonism, and as Shelley became more and more imbued with mystical philosophy, it was to Newtonian science that he turned. This evolution is apparent if *Queen Mab* and *Prometheus Unbound* are compared—extremes, to be sure, but justly defining Shelley as he was when a boy, a curious mixture of idealism and scepticism, and Shelley in his maturity when he had effected a hard won fusion of the diverse elements of his belief.

But is *Prometheus* the ultimate expression of his philosophy, and if he meant it to be so why did he express himself so reconditely? The answer lies in the history of Shelley's disappointments in authorship. *Prometheus* he declared to be written for but five or six persons, the extent of the audience to which he could look with any confidence. In this instance he was unduly optimistic, for it is not on record that any one has ever understood the whole of it.

Shelley wrote *Prometheus* to please himself, wrote it because he must. It is packed with imagery and symbolism which, it is evident, carried very definite meanings to him but which are unintelligible to the reader without a key to them. Shelley provided no key. Mrs. Shelley tells us that he planned to write a body of notes as he had done for *Queen Mab*. This design he never carried out and the poem has remained an enigma. Yet it is a work with which Shelley said he was less dissatisfied than with any other of his compositions. He also remarked that it had cost him severe labor. These statements justify intense study to determine what he concealed within his symbols, his personifications, his subtle and exquisite lyrics.

That the scientific allusions once understood do not make the whole of the poem clear is evident. The Platonic elements are even more difficult to interpret. Nevertheless through the elucidation of the science much light is thrown upon Shelley's central theme, and the student feels justified in attempting to crack the other half of the nut, confident that the feat is possible and that the result will repay the labor. Few poems justify such pains, but *Prometheus Unbound* rewards the most arduous study. Lyrically it has long been regarded as one of the masterpieces of English literature. Philosophically it will also rank with the best once it is fully understood. A partial understanding of it justifies the statement.

In the ensuing pages, after a brief rehearsal of Shelley's youthful enthusiasm for science and recapitulation of the scientific allusions in *Queen Mab,* several chapters are devoted to sketching those aspects of the thought of Erasmus Darwin, Herschel, Newton, and Davy which seem to bear most closely upon *Prometheus Unbound.* Darwin and Davy are alluded to in Shelley's letters; Herschel, mentioned in the notes to *Queen Mab,* was the greatest contemporary astronomer; and Newtonian theory underlies the radical speculations of Shelley's time as to the nature of matter and energy, speculations which were quickened by the great advances in chemical and electrical science made at the end of the eighteenth century. To know the work of these scientists, even in a necessarily sketchy fashion, is to know a part of the background of scientific thought essential to an understanding of Shelley. In the light of this knowledge, Shelley's use of science in *Prometheus* is far more intelligible than it would otherwise be.

Following the chapter on Davy, a discussion of Beccaria and his discoveries in meteorology leads directly into Shelley's use of electrical phenomena in *Prometheus* and thence to the concept of matter there evidenced. The concluding chapters deal with Shelley's use of other scientific facts—chemical, astronomical, and geological in *Prometheus.* No attempt is made to discuss science as employed by Shelley in other poems save, incidentally, *The Cloud.* That *The Witch of Atlas* contains scientific lore very like that in *Prometheus* can, I believe, be shown, but the meaning of that fanciful and enigmatic poem waits upon a satisfactory interpretation of the whole of *Prometheus,* for both are saturated with Platonism.

Nearly the whole of the fourth act of *Prometheus,* and considerable portions of the earlier acts are, beneath their symbolism, scientific in import. The Spirit of the Earth symbolizes atmospheric electricity. An electrical theory of matter derived from Newton and Davy explains passages in the fourth act intelligible in no other terms. Astronomical allusions to the theories of Newton and Herschel are numerous. And there are divers passages based on chemistry and geology. The passages thus interpreted I have paralleled with numerous citations from various scientific writers, most of which carry conviction at sight. In instances of which the meaning is not certain I have marshalled my parallels to the most plausible interpretation. But I have endeavored to be as little dogmatic as possible, for however my readers may differ from me in the explanation of details they will, I believe, admit the general soundness of my demonstration. The weight of evidence is too great, the consistency of Shelley's employment of scientific fact and theory too notable, to be denied.

Perhaps I should add, too, lest the purpose and method of this book be misunderstood, that in interpreting lines and symbols in *Prometheus Unbound* I have confined myself to their scientific reading and have ignored the Platonic or neo-Platonic implications which the line or symbol may bear. Nor have I pointed out resemblances to the work of other poets. Shelley's lines in *Prometheus* often express a dual symbolism: they are both scientific and neo-Platonic in their import. And in their imagery they may be reminiscent of Milton or Spenser. A complete annotation of the poem, such as I hope some day to publish, would leave no important implication without its commentary. To attempt so much here I have thought impracticable. Once the scientific character of much of *Prometheus* is established, the way to the fuller understanding of the poem and to its exhaustive documentation is open. What now, in this book, may seem an over-emphasis, even a distortion, will then be rectified.

I wish to acknowledge my indebtedness to Mr. C. A. Brown of Purdue University for the use of several citations from his notes upon the science of Shelley's day, citations from scientific journals and encyclopedias chiefly; and to Mr. Martin J. Freeman of the University of Chicago for suggestions made while the book was in preparation.

CARL H. GRABO.

University of Chicago.

TABLE OF CONTENTS

"WHAT THE HILLS were to the youth of Wordsworth, a chemical laboratory was to Shelley. It is unfortunate that Shelley's literary critics have, in this respect, so little of Shelley in their own mentality. They tend to treat as a casual oddity of Shelley's nature what was, in fact, part of the main structure of his mind, permeating his poetry through and through. If Shelley had been born a hundred years later, the twentieth century would have seen a Newton among chemists."

A. N. Whitehead in *Science and the Modern World*.

A NEWTON AMONG POETS

CHAPTER I

SHELLEY'S BOYHOOD INTEREST IN SCIENCE

INTEREST ALWAYS attaches to the childhood of great men, though the drift-wood salvaged by biographers infrequently repays the effort. Of Shelley it would be valuable to know, more than anything else, the books which he first read. At a later time the circumstances which led to his interest in Plato and Godwin are known or can be guessed, but of his earlier passion for the occult and for science the sources are unknown. In the library at Field Place were, I suspect, books of which Mr. Timothy Shelley would have disapproved had he known of their existence and could he have understood them. Old Sir Bysshe, a much more intelligent and curious minded person, may have collected them, or so it is pleasant to surmise: books on alchemy, magic, Rosicrucianism; and, in science, Priestley's work on electricity, Erasmus Darwin's *Botanic Garden,* Newton's *Opticks* perhaps. These or similar works Shelley must have read at a very early age. His mind was colored by them, his imagination given its bent.

What is known of Shelley's childhood and youth is retold by Mr. Ingpen in his *Shelley in England.* From his pages I shall pick out those details which are relevant to my desired emphasis and briefly relate them. The interest that attaches to every detail of Shelley's youthful pursuit of chemistry and electricity derives from our appreciation of the importance of these studies to his ultimate philosophy as expressed in *Prometheus Unbound.* What might seem a merely boyish fancy, like a passion for war and piracy, we perceive in retrospect was of deep significance. Under slightly altered circumstances Shelley would have become a scientist. The interest in science which held him to his Oxford days found no later expression in experimentation. But the teachings of science combine with Plato and the humanitarian French philosophers to compose Shelley's philosophy.

There are anecdotes of Shelley at some early age filling a portable stove with inflammable liquids and carrying it about, on one occasion setting fire to the butler. Again, in his boyhood—at an age not given—he endeavored to cure his sister's chilblains by means of an electric battery. Whether these youthful experiments were conducted before he began to attend Syon House academy or after does not appear; presumably after, when his interest in science was either aroused or strengthened by the lectures of Adam Walker, a self-taught natural philosopher. Walker lectured on astronomy, expressed a belief in the existence of other habitable globes like our own, and displayed the wonders of the solar microscope.

The solar microscope was an instrument combining the powers of a microscope and a camera obscura or magic lantern. The magnified object was thrown upon the wall or screen in a darkened room. Shelley at some later date acquired such an instrument and Hogg tells of him, when in London, retrieving it from a pawnshop to which it had gone when he needed money to relieve an old man in want. Shelley was very glad to get it again, Hogg observes. It is an incident symbolical, after Shelley's own manner of creating symbols, of his scale of values. Absorbed early in science and at Oxford experimenting in his rooms with chemistry and electricity, the scientific interest was subordinate to his passion for humanity. It was the reformer in Shelley which supplanted, though it did not destroy, the scientist.

Mr. Ingpen cites a sentence from Adam Walker's *Analysis of a Course of Lectures on Natural and Experimental Philosophy*.[1] Of the planets: "Who can doubt therefore but they

[1] Ingpen, *Shelley in England*, 48.

are inhabited, as well as all the worlds of the other system? How much too big is this idea for the human imagination!" This is Shelley's later belief as expressed in *Prometheus*, a belief strengthened by the authority of the great astronomer, Herschel.

At Eton Shelley is said to have "passed much of his leisure in the study of the occult sciences, natural philosophy, and chemistry; his pocket money was spent on books 'relative to these pursuits, on chemical apparatus and materials,' and many of the books treated of magic and witchcraft."[2] In his second letter to Godwin, recounting his education and intellectual interests Shelley writes: "Ancient books of chemistry and magic were perused with an enthusiasm of wonder, almost amounting to belief."

This early passion for the occult and the marvelous must be remembered in appraising Shelley's later use of science in *Prometheus*. His imagination fed on wonders. Rivalling his interest in magic and science was his boyish passion for the Gothic romance; his earliest writings which are of any value whatsoever were the two novels imitative of "Rosa Matilda." Shelley was highly imaginative, even credulous. The transition of his interest from the occult to the scientific is by way of this love for the marvelous, for the new sciences of chemistry and electricity promised greater marvels than alchemy, marvels much more authentic, more possible of immediate realization. It is natural, therefore, that in the philosophy of *Prometheus*, blent of humanitarian radicalism, Platonism, occultism, and science, the more radical speculations of scientific philosophy rather than its conservative findings should have chief place. Yet fanciful as some of these speculations then seemed, time has shown them to be close to the mark.

[2] *Ibid.*, 63.

The guesses of Newton, Erasmus Darwin, and Davy became the theories of a later time.

Helen Shelley's memory of her brother with face and hands blackened in some experiment by lunar caustic is assigned by Mr. Ingpen to Shelley's Eton days when his chemical investigations were largely restricted to his vacations at home. The Eton authorities disapproved of the pursuit of any knowledge other than that prescribed by the curriculum, in which science then had no place. Shelley's father is on record as having returned to Medwin senior a book on chemistry borrowed by Percy as it was 'a forbidden thing at Eton.' Nevertheless Shelley apparently violated the rules of the school, for one anecdote tells of his tutor surprising him in an experiment and as being thrown against the wall upon grasping a charged electrical machine. Anecdotes of this order have their variants which need not be cited. All agree that Shelley was given to experiments in chemistry and electricity. Medwin states that Shelley made an electrical kite after Franklin's famous example and for the same purpose, to draw lightning from the clouds.

Other legends ascribe to Shelley setting a tree on fire by means of gunpowder and a burning glass, and of having employed a tinker to aid him in the construction of a steam engine, which burst. His interest in astronomy is supposed to have been rearoused by a lecture given at Eton by the Adam Walker of Syon House days. Mr. Ingpen believes that Shelley was encouraged in his study of chemistry and astronomy by Dr. James Lind, the Eton tutor whom Shelley so greatly admired and through whom he is supposed to have got his first knowledge of Godwin's *Political Justice*.

At Eton Shelley read Lucretius and translated parts of Pliny's *Natural History*. I have detected no echoes of Lucretius in *Prometheus*, though there may well be some which a closer examination would reveal. Nevertheless I believe *De Rerum Natura* to be highly important in Shelley's poetic development. Lucretius makes good poetry and philosophy from the science of his time. Later Shelley was to read Erasmus Darwin, whose science was good and whose poetry was bad. With the memory of Lucretius to inspire confidence he need nevertheless not have feared to put scientific ideas into verse. Failure lay not in the ideas but in the form in which they were expressed.

There is, moreover, a broad resemblance between *De Rerum Natura* and *Prometheus Unbound.* Both are written in disrespect of the accepted gods. Both seek to enfranchise man through reliance upon his own powers. Both glorify science and belittle conventional theology. The disbelief of Lucretius in the ancient gods is like Shelley's disbelief in the modern god of man's creation, the god not of nature and law but fabricated of fear, hate, and violence, an anarchic god.

Hogg's record of his Oxford days with Shelley is full of references to Shelley's preoccupation with science. At their first meeting Shelley talked of chemistry and shortly departed to attend a lecture upon mineralogy whence he returned much disappointed. The lecturer "talked about nothing but stones, stones, stones, stones, nothing but stones, and so drily."

It is to Hogg, I believe, that we may ascribe the belief so long and so erroneously held, that Shelley's enthusiasm for science was but a foible of a mercurial and fantastic nature. Hogg, it is evident, knew nothing whatsoever about science. Shelley's talk revealed to him a new world, a mad unreasonable world unknown to classical literature. To Shelley, modern science, electricity in particular, was the agent which was to transform the earth. He pictured—

An unfruitful region being transmuted into a land of exuberant plenty; the arid wastes of Africa refreshed by a copious supply of water. " It will," he said, "perhaps be possible at no very distant date to produce heat at will and to warm the most ungenial climates as we now raise the temperature of our apartments to whatever degree we may deem agreeable or salutary. But if this be too much to anticipate, at any rate we may expect 'to provide ourselves cheaply with a fund of heat that will supersede our costly and inconvenient fuel, and will suffice to warm our habitations, for culinary purposes and for the various demands for the mechanical arts' " . . . "What a mighty instrument would electricity be in the hands of him who knew how to wield it . . . by electrical kites we may draw down the lightning from heaven.

The galvanic battery is a new engine . . . what will not an extraordinary combination of troughs of colossal magnitude, a well arranged system of hundreds of metallic plates effect? The balloon has not yet received the perfection of which it is surely capable; the art of navigating the air is in its first and most helpless infancy. It promises prodigious facilities for locomotion, and will enable us to traverse vast tracts with ease and rapidity, and to explore unknown countries without difficulty. Why are we still so ignorant of the interior of Africa?—Why do we not despatch intrepid aeronauts to cross it in every direction, and to survey the whole peninsula in a few weeks? The shadow of the first balloon, which a vertical sun would project precisely beneath it, as it glides silently over that hitherto unhappy country, would virtually emancipate every slave, and would annihilate slavery forever.[3]

Hogg records also that Shelley declared he knew nothing of mathematics "and treated the whole notion of their paramount importance with contempt." Hogg is not always trustworthy and "contempt" seems a strong word in view of Shelley's interest in astronomy. If ever he held such a contempt he later outgrew it, for in his last years he mentions in a letter that he and Mary intend to take up the study of mathematics.[4]

The most humorous aspect of Hogg's amusing description of Shelley's scientific fancies is his own complete ignorance

[3] Cited by Ingpen, 108-9.
[4] Letter to John and Maria Gisborne, Feb. 9, 1820.

of their justification in the scientific theory of the day. Even at the time of writing his reminiscences, over a quarter of a century later, he seems to have been unaware that twenty-five years before that memorable night in Shelley's Oxford rooms experimenters had demonstrated, or so they thought, the power of electricity to stimulate the growth of plants; and Erasmus Darwin had predicted the airplane driven by an engine whose motive power should be some explosive substance. However fanciful these ideas, they were, therefore, not Shelley's. Shelley was a well-read youth whose imagination had been fired by the marvels and possibilities of science and who dreamed of a new and better world in which they were to be put to the service of man.

Hogg's description of Shelley's room again stresses Shelley's preoccupation with scientific pursuits:

Books, boots, papers, shoes, philosophical instruments, clothes, pistols, linen, crockery, ammunition, and phials innumerable, with money, stockings, prints, crucibles, bags, and boxes, were scattered on the floor and in every place; as if the young chemist, in order to analyze the mystery of creation, had endeavored first to reconstruct the primeval chaos. The tables and especially the carpet were already stained with large spots of various hues, which frequently proclaimed the agency of fire. An electrical machine, an air-pump, the galvanic trough, a solar microscope, and large glass jars and receivers were conspicuous amidst the mass of matter. Upon the table by his side were some books lying open, several letters, a bundle of new pens, and a bottle of Japan ink, that served as an inkstand. . . . Two piles of books supported the tongs, and these upheld a small glass retort above an argand lamp. I had not been seated many minutes before the liquor in the vessel boiled over, adding fresh stains to the table, and rising in fumes with a most disagreeable odour. Shelley snatched the glass quickly and, dashing it in pieces among the ashes under the g ate, increased the unpleasant and penetrating effluvium.[5]

[5] Cited by Ingpen, 110-111.

Shelley is quoted by Hogg as asserting that chemistry was the only science which deserved to be studied. He conducted experiments in his rooms, which bore the marks of his labors. There were holes burned in the carpets and in the floor.

His rooms were preferred because there his philosophical apparatus was at hand, and he was able at any moment to ascertain by actual experiment the value of some new idea that rushed into his brain. He spent much of his time and money at this time in the assiduous cultivation of chemistry. These chemical operations seemed to an unskilled observer to promise nothing but disasters.[6]

On one occasion Hogg was horrified to discover in a cup into which he was about to pour tea a seven-shilling piece partly dissolved by *aqua regia.* His nerves were not soothed upon Shelley's declaring that he had at Eton inadvertently swallowed mineral poisons—perhaps arsenic—with a resultant shock to his system from which he feared he should never entirely recover.[7]

There are a few other of Hogg's reminiscences which bear testimony to Shelley's preoccupation with science while at Oxford. By way of a joke he endeavored to electrify the son of his scout. He addressed inquiries on chemical subjects by letter in the manner he shortly afterwards employed with such disastrous consequences in matters theological, signing some fictitious name to his epistles. But these are only straws in the wind. Of deeper interest is Hogg's statement as to Shelley's prowess as a reader. Hogg averred that Shelley sometimes read sixteen hours out of the twenty-four. Trelawny's testimony at a later day is to much the same effect. Given Shelley's mind and retentive memory it is possible then to believe that at the age of thirty when he died, or at twenty-six when he composed *Prometheus,* he knew so much

---

[6] Cited by Ingpen, 112.
[7] *Ibid.,* 113.

as he seems to have known of ancient and modern literature and philosophy and had withal so extensive a reading knowledge of science.

There are two further citations, one from Hogg, and another from a letter of Shelley to Hogg, which I wish to make, believing them to be significant of Shelley's mind and of scientific beliefs which find expression later in *Prometheus*. Shelley, says Hogg, "believed implicitly every assertion, so that it was improbable, and incredible, exulting in the success of his philosophic doubts, when like the calmest and most suspicious of analysts he refused to admit, without strict proof, propositions that many, who are not deficient in metaphysical prudence, account obvious and self-evident."[8]

The letter in part:[9]

Before we deny or believe the existence of anything, it is necessary that we should have a tolerably clear idea of what it is. The word 'God,' a vague word, has been, and will continue to be, the source of numberless errors, until it is erased from the nomenclature of philosophy. Does it not imply "the soul of the Universe, the intelligent and *necessarily* beneficent actuating principle?" This it is impossible not to believe in; I may not be able to adduce proofs; but I think that the leaf of a tree, the meanest insect on which we trample, are, in themselves, arguments more conclusive than any which can be advanced, that some vast intellect animates infinity. If we disbelieve *this,* the strongest argument in support of the existence of a future state instantly becomes annihilated. I confess that I think Pope's
        "All are but parts of one stupendous whole"
something more than poetry. It has ever been my favorite theory.

He then proceeds to denounce the theory of personal immortality and somewhat obscurely to proclaim a belief in "Love, love, *infinite in extent*" which "should be the reward,"

[8] *Ibid.,* 133.
[9] Shelley to Hogg, Jan. 3, 1811.

a reward which cannot arise "spontaneously, as a necessary appendage to our nature" but which presupposes "a first cause—a God." It is an incoherent letter. "Never," he declares, "will I forgive intolerance! . . . I expect to gratify some of this insatiable feeling in poetry." And a final passage:

> Do you allow that some *supernatural* power actuates the organization of physical causes? . . . If this Deity thus influences the action of the Spirits (if I may be allowed the expression) which take care of minor events . . . why is it *not* the soul of the Universe; in what is it not analogous to the soul of man? Why *too* is *not* gravitation the soul of a clock? . . . I think we may not inaptly define *Soul* as the most supreme, superior, and distinguished abstract appendage to the nature of anything.

There are clear evidences in this that Shelley, whether directly or indirectly, had already some knowledge of Newtonian speculation. Evident, too, are the seeds of ideas which were destined later to bear fruit in *Prometheus Unbound,* in which the Spirit of the Earth is made to be electricity.

Upon Shelley's expulsion from Oxford he put away his playthings which, soon, had he pursued the scholarly life might have become his tools. The college authorities probably destroyed a chemist and helped to create a poet. No virtue is theirs, however great the world's gain; if, indeed, it is a gain, for Shelley might, as Mr. Whitehead has affirmed, have become great among scientists. Why he turned from science as a vocation is easily explained. He had not the basic training nor the means easily to acquire it. Yet these were obstacles he could have overcome had his heart been set on so doing. Other interests diverted him, especially the passion to reform the world, which in his own brief experience he had found to be intolerant and unjust; the acquisition, too, of a wife and family; emotional disturbances, diverse and harrowing; conflicts with his family, and with the courts;

fear of imprisonment for debt; ill health—the reasons why, until the year 1818, Shelley could not become a scientist are sufficient.

When in the Spring of 1818, in Italy, Shelley entered upon the last brilliant creative period of his life he was, though young in years, old in emotional experience and, in his intellectual acquisitions, mature. He felt that he had lived a hundred years. His desire to reform the world had been thwarted by his exile. He thought himself a failure. The poetic power which he had discovered in himself was unappreciated by others. Few read his works and of these the greater number condemned him as both immoral and obscure. His task was to find peace and rest and to reconcile in some unified and consistent philosophy all the warring doubts and beliefs which had beset him ever since his precocious boyhood. In this philosophy, the ideas of science must have a place, but there is no evidence that Shelley longer thought of a career as an experimental investigator in chemistry or electricity. The philosophy of science, however, contributed to his ultimate great achievement as philosopher-poet.

CHAPTER II

QUEEN MAB, A PRECURSOR OF PROMETHEUS UNBOUND

To UNDERSTAND what that achievement was, its character and greatness, it is necessary to return to the one early poem in which Shelley expresses some of his scientific knowledge and beliefs, *Queen Mab,* and to point out certain passages which have their successors in *Prometheus.* In his last years Shelley professed little recollection of and no interest in *Queen Mab,* regarding it as a youthful indiscretion better forgotten. Yet its verse is better, I believe, than is generally conceded. As the work of a boy of eighteen or so it is remarkable. And to the student of Shelley it is invaluable, for in it are first expressed those ideas which constitute the themes of his later and better work. Shelley's philosophy gains tremendously in subtlety and in refinement of expression during the ten years of his poetic activity. But his fundamental attitudes and beliefs either remain unchanged or evolve slowly and intelligibly. Therefore to consider some of the ideas contained in *Queen Mab* is to make *Prometheus* more easily understood.

Of scientific facts introduced the astronomical are chief. The journey of the spirit of Ianthe in the magic car depicts the sublimity and the vastness of the stellar universe in terms of the new astronomy. I shall cite four instances of Shelley's description with notes to two of them:

> Seemed it, that the chariot's way
> Lay through the midst of an immense concave,
> Radiant with million constellations, tinged
>   With shades of infinite colour,
>   And semicircled with a belt
>   Flashing incessant meteors.
>
> Q. M. I. ll. 231-236.

Again:

> . . . and soon appeared
> Such tiny twinklers as the planet orbs
> That there attendant on the solar power
> With borrowed light pursued their narrower way.
>
> *Q. M.* IX. ll. 222-225.

To the next is appended a long note of which I quote the greater part. Shelley's youthful display of encyclopedic information is rather charming and naïve.

> Whilst round the chariot's way
> Innumerable systems rolled.
>
> *Q. M.* I. ll. 252-253.

The plurality of worlds,—the indefinite immensity of the universe is a most awful subject of contemplation. . . . All that miserable tale of the Devil, and Eve, and an intercessor, with the childish mummeries of the God of the Jews, is irreconcilable with the knowledge of the stars. . . . The nearest of the fixed stars is inconceivably distant from the earth, and they are probably proportionably distant from each other. By a calculation of the velocity of light, Sirius is supposed to be at least 54,244,000,000,000 miles from the earth.[1] That which appears only like a thin and silvery cloud streaking the heaven, is, in effect composed of innumerable clusters of suns, each shining with its own light, and illuminating numbers of planets that revolve around them. Millions and millions of suns are ranged around us, all attended by innumerable worlds, yet calm, regular, and harmonious, all keeping the paths of immutable necessity.

The next instance is important, for it reveals Shelley's interest in the phenomena of light in relation to the atmosphere. Shelley was either familiar with Newton's *Opticks* or later works derived therefrom. I shall have occasion in the discussion of *Prometheus* to point out the instances in which this knowledge is implied.

[1] See Nicholson's *Encyclopedia,* article Light.

> The sun's unclouded orb
> Rolled through the black concave.
>
> *Q. M.* I. ll. 242-243.

Beyond our atmosphere the sun would appear a rayless orb of fire
in the midst of a black concave. The equal diffusion of its light
on earth is owing to the refraction of the rays by the atmosphere,
and their reflection from other bodies. Light consists either of
vibrations propagated through a subtle medium, or of numerous
minute particles repelled in all directions from the luminous body.
. . . Some idea may be gained of the immense distance of the
fixed stars, when it is computed that many years would elapse
before light could reach this earth from the nearest of them. . . .

The emotion aroused by the contemplation of the stellar
universe and the philosophy which it suggests is in *Queen Mab*
precisely that of Meredith in *Lucifer in Starlight*. The stars
march in their ancient track an "army of unalterable law."

> Countless and unending orbs
> In mazy motion intermingled,
> Yet still fulfilled immutably
>   Eternal nature's law.
> Above, below, around
> The circling systems formed
> A wilderness of harmony;
> Each with undeviating aim,
> In eloquent silence, through the depths of space
> Pursued its wondrous way.
>
> *Q. M.* II. ll. 73-82.

A yet longer and more rhetorical passage elaborates the
same theme and links the movements of the stars with the
leaf and the worm. Nature, in this philosophy, is coherent,
consistent, unified.

> Innumerable systems rolled,
> And countless spheres diffused
> An ever-varying glory.
> It was a sight of wonder: some

Were hornèd like the crescent moon;
Some shed a mild and silver beam
Like Hesperus o'er the western sea;
Some dash'd athwart with trains of flame,
Like worlds to death and ruin driven;
Some shone like suns, and as the chariot passed,
Eclipsed all other light.

Spirit of Nature! here!
In this interminable wilderness
Of worlds, at whose immensity
Even soaring fancy staggers,
Here is thy fitting temple.
Yet not the lightest leaf
That quivers to the passing breeze
Is less instinct with thee:
Yet not the meanest worm
That lurks in graves and fattens on the dead
Less shares thy eternal breath.
Spirit of Nature! thou!
Imperishable as this scene,
Here is thy fitting temple.

Q. M. I. ll. 253-277.

The heavens would seem to confess the majesty of God. But not so. Shelley is careful to deny His existence.

There is no God!
. . . . . .
. . . infinity within,
Infinity without, belie creation;
The exterminable spirit it contains
Is nature's only God. . . .

Q. M. VII. ll. 13-24.

To this passage he subscribes a note that his meaning may be clear:

This negation must be understood solely to affect a creative Deity. The hypothesis of a pervading Spirit, coeternal with the universe, remains unshaken.

Apparently what Shelley wishes to deny is the God of the Christians, the God of the Book of Genesis. The conception of God, under another name, is admissible. This God is the Spirit of Nature or the Soul of the Universe.

> Throughout this varied and eternal world
> Soul is the only element: the block
> That for uncounted ages has remained
> The moveless pillar of a mountain's weight
> Is active, living spirit. Every grain
> Is sentient both in unity and part,
> And the minutest atom comprehends
> A world of loves and hatreds; these beget
> Evil and good: hence truth and falsehood spring;
> Hence will and thought and action, all the germs
> Of pain or pleasure, sympathy or hate,
> That variegate the eternal universe.
> Soul is not more polluted than the beams
> Of heaven's pure orb, ere round their rapid lines
> The taint of earth-born atmospheres arise.
>
> $Q. M.$ IV. ll. 139-153.

The idea is several times repeated: There is one consistent law which holds for the entire universe; there is a soul or spirit which animates all things.

> Throughout these infinite orbs of mingling light,
> Of which yon earth is one, is wide diffused
> A spirit of activity and life,
> That knows no term, cessation, or decay;
> That fades not when the lamp of earthly life,
> Extinguished in the dampness of the grave,
> A while there slumbers . . .
>
> .   .   .   .   .   .
>
> But active, stedfast, and eternal, still

Guides the fierce whirlwind, in the tempest roars,
Cheers in the day, breathes in the balmy groves,
Strengthens in health, and poisons in disease;
And in the storm of change, that ceaselessly
Rolls round the eternal universe, and shakes
Its undecaying battlement, presides,
Apportioning with irresistible law
The place each spring of its machine shall fill.

                    Q. M. VI. ll. 146-164.

The name for this God or Law is commonly, in the school of Holbach, Necessity. A modern scientist probably is unable to feel a warm personal attachment to this deity, but the eighteenth century sceptics found it a palatable substitute for the God of the church. It is addressed with a devotional fervor.

Spirit of Nature! all-sufficing Power,
Necessity! thou mother of the world!
Unlike the God of human error, thou
Requirest no prayers or praises . . .

.   .   .   .   .

. . . all that the wide world contains
Are but thy passive instruments, and thou
Regard'st them all with an impartial eye.

                    Q. M. VI. ll. 197-216.

All nature is animated by this spirit or abstraction—it is difficult to determine which:

How wonderful! that even
The passions, prejudices, interests
That sway the meanest being, the weak touch
    That moves the finest nerve,
    And in one human brain
Causes the faintest thought, becomes a link
    In the great chain of nature.

                    Q. M. II. ll. 102-108.

It is at this point that the concepts of incompatible philosophies involve the youthful Shelley in contradictions which are irreconcilable. Nature is all law and necessity. Nature is beautiful and good. What then of man, who obviously is neither beautiful nor good? The psychological doctrine of Locke, that of the mind at birth being a *tabula rasa,* suggested that man might be good if subjected to the proper influences. He is bad because his education and environment are bad. The thing to do is to better his education and improve his environment. But how do this in a world governed by the iron law of necessity, in which the fall of every leaf and every lightest thought is an inescapable consequence of an infinite series of causes? Here is a dilemma unsolved, so far as I am aware, by any thinker of the revolutionary school. Shelley certainly does not solve it.

> Look on yonder earth:
> The golden harvests spring; the unfailing sun
> Sheds light and life; the fruits, the flowers, the trees,
> Arise in due succession; all things speak
> Peace, harmony, and love. The universe,
> In nature's silent eloquence, declares
> That all fulfill the works of love and joy,—
> All but the outcast, man.
>
> *Q. M.* III. ll. 192-199.

It would seem, then, that man is the one blot on creation, the one defect in a perfect universe. Yet once he was good, in the golden age before social institutions were invented. Clearly there was a Fall, though not such as that depicted in the Bible. Shelley in a long and documented note surmises that it was man's adoption of a meat diet which was the cause of the loss of Eden and all our woe. Man must have likewise seduced the animals to sin, for, forgetful of those passages in which he has described the beauty and innocence of Nature, Shelley thus depicts the evolution from the present misery of the world to the golden age which is to be:

> All things are recreated, and the flame
> Of consentaneous love inspires all life;
>
> .   .   .   .
>
> The lion now forgets to thirst for blood:
> There might you see him sporting in the sun
> Beside the dreadless kid; his claws are sheathed,
> His teeth are harmless, custom's force has made
> His nature as the nature of a lamb.
>
> *Q. M.* VIII. ll. 107-128.

It is impossible to reconcile an evolutionary natural philosophy with the social contract theory of Rousseau, and a theory of perfectibility with the myth of a golden age. Shelley, ardent humanitarian and, at the same time, student of science seeks to fuse the two. He was a boy of genius, but nevertheless a boy; the effort failed. It was not until his maturity that he succeeded—if he did succeed—in blending the diverse elements of his beliefs into a unity. The determination of that ultimate philosophy I shall not seek in this place nor, indeed, wholly in this book, which is concerned with the scientific aspects of Shelley's thought. But the problem itself needs to be perceived in order that the implications of Shelley's scientific beliefs may be understood.

Let me, therefore, cite a few further passages confirmatory of Shelley's evolutionary philosophy of nature, incompatible as that may be with other of his statements.

> Spirit of Nature! thou
> Life of interminable multitudes;
> Soul of those mighty spheres
> Whose changeless paths thro' Heaven's deep silence lie;
> Soul of that smallest being,
> The dwelling of whose life
> Is one faint April sun-gleam;—

> Man, like these passive things,
> Thy will unconsciously fulfilleth;
>   Like theirs, his age of endless peace,
>   Which time is fast maturing,
>   Will swiftly, surely come;
> And the unbounded frame, which thou pervadest,
>   Will be without a flaw
> Marring its perfect symmetry.
>
> *Q. M.* III. ll. 226-240.

Man's evolution from his present state to the promised perfection which is to be is the vision granted the Spirit of Ianthe. The next brief passages explicitly define the evolutionary, rather than the cataclysmic, nature of the change.

> Thus human beings were perfected, and earth,
> Even as a child beneath its mother's love,
> Was strengthened in all excellence, and grew
> Fairer and nobler with each passing year.
>
> *Q. M.* IX. ll. 134-137.

Another:

> Let virtue teach thee firmly to pursue
> The gradual paths of an aspiring change:
>
> *Q. M.* IX. ll. 147-148.

And a last instance:

> [Man] Who stands amid the ever-varying world,
> The burthen or the glory of the earth;
> He chief perceives the change, his being notes
> The gradual renovation, and defines
> Each movement of its progress on his mind.
>
> *Q. M.* VIII. ll. 140-144.

That Shelley was familiar with Erasmus Darwin's work at this time we know from a letter to Hogg quoted in the next chapter. But there are in *Queen Mab* a few verbal echoes which substantiate the fact. Shelley's line

Making the earth a slaughter house
                    Q. M. VII. l. 48.

is clearly reminiscent of Darwin's line

And one great Slaughter-house the warring world.
                    Temple of Nature, IV. l. 66.

Again Shelley's lines

Yon monarch in his solitary pomp
Was but the mushroom of a summer day
                    Q. M. IX. ll. 31-32.

recall a similar association of ideas in Darwin

Hence when a Monarch or a mushroom dies
                    Temple of Nature, IV. l. 383.

Such verbal echoes are rather rare in Shelley, whose indebtedness to others usually takes the form of ideas rather than phrases. As an instance in point the following parallel might be drawn though not pressed:

There's not one atom of yon earth
    But once was living man;
Nor the minutest drop of rain,
That hangeth in its thinnest cloud,
    But flowed in human veins.
                    Q. M. II. ll. 211-215.

Darwin in *The Temple of Nature* has a long passage depicting the changes of matter in which he shows how the mountains and the coral islands

Were built by myriad nations of the deep

concluding with the lines

Thus the tall mountains, that emboss the lands,
Huge isles of rock, and continents of sands.

Whose dim extent eludes the inquiring sight,
Are mighty monuments of past delight.

Temple of Nature, IV. ll. 447-450.

That all matter was once a part of some living creature is the idea common to both.

Shelley's belief, however, is that matter itself is animate, that the atom is endowed with life:

I tell thee that those living things,
To whom the fragile blade of grass,
That springeth in the morn
And perisheth ere noon,
Is an unbounded world;
I tell thee that those viewless beings,
Whose mansion is the smallest particle
Of the impassive atmosphere,
Think, feel and live like man;

Q. M. II. ll. 226-234.

This same belief forms an important part of the philosophy of *Prometheus,* in the discussion of which I shall have more to say of it. It suffices here to remark that the idea is expressed by Darwin, perhaps rather as a poetic figure than a genuine scientific belief, and that in origin it is at best semi-scientific or occult. In Paracelsus and the Rosicrucians it assumes an important place. It is impossible in this discussion to confine the argument wholly to Shelley's science, for his scientific beliefs are overlapped with his occult and mystical beliefs and modified thereby. As well as I can I endeavor to show the line of demarcation. As an instance the following passage and its note is in point.

To the red and baleful sun
That faintly twinkles there

Q. M. VI. ll. 45-46.

The north polar star to which the axis of the earth in its present state of obliquity points. It is exceedingly probable from many

considerations that this obliquity will gradually diminish until the
equator coincides with the ecliptic; the nights and days will then
become equal on the earth throughout the year, and probably the
seasons also. There is no great extravagance in presuming that the
progress of the perpendicularity of the poles may be as rapid as
the progress of intellect; or *that there should be a perfect identity
between the moral and physical improvement of the human
species.* [Italics mine.] It is certain that wisdom is not compatible
with disease, and that, in the present state of the climates of the
earth, health, in the true and comprehensive sense of the word, is
out of the reach of civilized man. Astronomy teaches us that the
earth is now in its progress, and that the poles are every year becoming more and more perpendicular to the ecliptic. The strong
evidence afforded by the history of mythology and geological researches that some event of this nature has taken place already
affords a strong presumption that this progress is not merely an
oscillation, as has been surmised by some late astronomers.[2] Bones
of animals peculiar to the torrid zone have been found in the north
of Siberia and on the banks of the river Ohio. Plants have been
found in the fossil state in the interior of Germany, which demand
the present climate of Hindostan for their production.[3] The researches of M. Bailly[4] established the existence of a people who
inhabited a tract in Tartary 49° north latitude, of greater antiquity
than either the Indians, the Chinese, or the Chaldeans, from
whom these nations derived their sciences and theology. We
find from the testimony of ancient writers that Britain, Germany,
and France were much colder than at present, and that their great
rivers were annually frozen over. Astronomy teaches us also that
since this period the obliquity of the earth's position has been
considerably diminished.

The interest of the passage lies partly in its revelation of
Shelley's knowledge of astronomy and of the scientific books
he had read, and, in the lines italicized, of his evolutionary,
yet withal mystical, belief in the accord of the physical with

[2] Laplace, *Système du Monde.*
[3] Cabanis, *Rapports du Physique et du Moral de l'Homme,* II, 406.
[4] Bailly, *Letters sur les Sciences, à Voltaire.*

the moral improvement of mankind. That it is a belief to
which Shelley clung is evidenced in *Prometheus*. Once
Prometheus has made a moral conquest of himself and for-
given his enemy, not only is Jupiter overthrown but all life
forms attain physical and moral perfection.

> All things had put their evil nature off
> *Prometheus Unbound*, III. 4, l. 77.

There are other evidences that the ideas which Shelley
believed when he wrote *Queen Mab* were those to which
he clung at a later day, however much his expression of them
matured and improved in subtlety and beauty. Likewise
in *Queen Mab* are expressed Shelley's hatred of marriage as an
institution and his advocacy of a virtuous promiscuity, ideas
which reappear, more cautiously phrased, in *Prometheus*. The
picture drawn by Queen Mab of a regenerate and happy earth,
in the golden age to be, is indeed, very like the picture of the
Promethean age, both in its physical and its moral aspects.

> The habitable earth is full of bliss;
> Those wastes of frozen billows that were hurled
> By everlasting snow-storms round the poles,
> Where matter dared not vegetate or live,
> But ceaseless frost round the vast solitude
> Bound its broad zone of stillness, are unloosed;
> And fragrant zephyrs there from spicy isles
> Ruffle the placid ocean-deep. . . .
> *Q. M.* VIII. ll. 58-65.

In *Prometheus Unbound* earth and moon, after the liberation of Prometheus, became warm and habitable. Shelley
depicts them as reliving their youth, his scientific authority
being, presumably, Darwin, who believed that at one stage in
the earth's history the climate was equable from pole to pole
and there were no violent storms, a recollection of which
time, lingering in the memory of the race, was the origin of

the legend of the Garden of Eden. There are other parallels. In Queen Mab's description of the golden age to come

> Mild was the slow necessity of death
>
> *Q. M.* IX. l. 57.

In *Prometheus,* in the golden age before the advent of Jupiter,

> Disease drank and slept. Death grew like sleep.
>
> *P. U.* II. 4, l. 86.

Again the Promethean age is characterized by man's mastery of nature and the elements: "All things confess his strength;" "the lightning is his slave;" he compels the "elements with adamantine stress." In *Queen Mab*

> . . . happiness
> And science dawn though late upon the earth.
>
> *Q. M.* VIII. ll. 227-228.

and

> Whilst every shape and mode of matter lends
> Its force to the omnipotence of mind.
>
> *Q. M.* VIII. ll. 235-236.

One passage in *Queen Mab* becomes wholly intelligible only in the light of Shelley's subsequent use of the same conception in *Prometheus.*

> The magic car moved on—
> From the celestial hoofs
> The atmosphere in flaming sparkles flew,
> And where the burning wheels
> Eddied above the mountain's loftiest peak,
> Was traced a line of lightning.
>
> *Q. M.* I. ll. 212-217.

The magic car is very like the car driven by the Spirit of the Hour in *Prometheus* whose

> . . . coursers are fed with the lightning
> They drink of the whirlwind's stream
>   *P. U.* II. 4, ll. 163-164.

In both, the speed and energy are electric. But of this more in its place when I discuss Shelley's use of electricity in *Prometheus*.

Queen Mab is an odd medley of Godwin, Holbach, Rousseau, and natural science. As I have sought to demonstrate, certain of these components are logically irreconcilable. The poem is an eloquent piece of rhetoric, more impassioned than convincing. The elements of Shelley's philosophy are there, but the Platonic solvent which is to blend and unify them is lacking. Shelley, vaguely recalling the work nearly ten years later, dismissed it as of no importance, forgetting that in his boyhood, whose culmination *Queen Mab* epitomizes, lay the seeds of his mature beliefs.

I have pointed out some of the resemblances of *Queen Mab* to *Prometheus* in its vision of a golden age to come and its use of scientific matter. There is a further resemblance which, though not scientific, supports my general observation that the germs of Shelley's mature work are to be found in the work of his adolescence. Ahasuerus, with whom the Spirit of Ianthe converses, as Asia with Demogorgon, is an early personification of a theme which Shelley developed successively in *The Wandering Jew, Queen Mab, The Revolt of Islam,* and *Prometheus Unbound,* the theme of the rebel and heretic defying tyranny, whether secular or divine, and, though suffering torments, remaining master of his soul and in his steadfastness giving assurance of the tyrant's ultimate overthrow. It is Shelley's vision of the triumph of good over evil, and its most beautiful and profound expression is *Prometheus Unbound.*

Wholly to understand *Prometheus* demands a mastery of much if not all of Shelley's philosophic reading, a formidable task and one happily beyond the scope of this book. The succeeding chapters consider only certain of the scientific thinkers who most influenced him. A discussion of their ideas leads from natural philosophy into the realm of metaphysics in the instance of Newton; but the book, in the development of its theme, having indicated this and similar trespasses, is content to stop there. The elucidation of the scientific allusions in *Prometheus* deriving from a knowledge of these scientific philosophers is of itself a sufficient task, one moreover, as being susceptible of proof, more grateful than an elucidation of Shelley's mystical beliefs. The first of the writers to be considered is Erasmus Darwin, whose important relation to Shelley has been intimated. Two chapters are devoted to Darwin, one to his general scientific ideas, the other to his theory and proofs of organic evolution.

In Darwin and the other scientific writers taken up, together with the poetic drama *Prometheus Unbound* which they helped to create, lies a considerable part of the intellectual history of a great poet who died in his thirtieth year. I close this chapter sketching the notable work of Shelley's youth, *Queen Mab,* with an excerpt from one of the notes thereto, a passage which, like some others in Shelley, is strangely prophetic of his own life and death:

Thus the life of a man of virtue and talent, who should die in his thirtieth year, is with regard to his own feelings longer than that of a miserable priest-ridden slave who dreams out a century of dulness.[5]

[5] Excerpt from note to VIII. ll. 203-207.

CHAPTER III

ERASMUS DARWIN: I. GENERAL SCIENTIFIC IDEAS

IN A LETTER of July 28, 1811 to Hogg, Shelley writes, "I do not see a soul; all is gloomy and desolate. I amuse myself, however, with reading Darwin, climbing rocks, and exploring scenery. Amusement!" Again in a letter to Rickman, the bookseller, Dec. 24, 1812, Shelley orders Darwin's *The Temple of Nature*. Reminiscences of this work are detectable in at least two lines of *Queen Mab*.[1] And parallels sufficiently explicit are to be found between *The Botanic Garden* and *Prometheus Unbound*. It suffices that Shelley was familiar with Darwin's two scientific epics and, it is likely, had read also the *Zoonomia,* Darwin's medical work, which contains scientific speculations of various sorts, especially such as support his theory of evolution.

Similarities in *Prometheus Unbound* of subject matter and imagery to specific passages of Darwin's verse will later be discussed. I wish here, in the first of two chapters, to give in general terms the substance of Darwin's chief works, the way in which he makes use of scientific ideas for the purpose of poetry, and, more especially, the range and originality of his speculations; and in a second chapter to discuss his theory and proofs of organic evolution, in which he so strikingly anticipates the work of Lamarck.

Erasmus Darwin, grandfather of Charles Darwin, was an original scientific observer and thinker, sceptical, imaginative, and curious minded in the best eighteenth century manner. The youthful Shelley, already experimentally interested in chemistry and electricity, and absorbed, likewise,

[1] See p. 23.

in the occult, seeking to evoke the devil by the exercise of magic, found, I believe, in Darwin's speculations food for the imagination, and also, through Darwin's copious notes and citations, easy access to the scientific writers of the day. Darwin's footnotes and "additional notes" range over the whole field of science. His point of view and philosophy were, moreover, strictly evolutionary, and his facts and theories link eighteenth century science with the thought of the early Greek philosophers. To read Darwin was, for Shelley, to synthesize much of his reading in science and philosophy. The fact that in the decade after his death Darwin's evolutionary ideas fell into general disrepute Shelley either did not know, or knowing, disregarded. By the year 1818 Darwin was looked upon largely as a scientific and literary oddity. Yet the evidence in *Prometheus* of Darwin's extensive influence is so unmistakable that we are forced to believe either that Shelley's scientific reading was not up to date or that, with greater imaginative perception and philosophic grasp than most of his contemporaries, he perceived the essential originality and soundness of Darwin's work. Shelley, I conceive, apprehended truth through the instrumentality of the imagination, and few scientific writers stir the imagination so profoundly as does Erasmus Darwin even today, for he sought to grasp this sorry scheme of things entire.

Anna Seward, friend and disciple of the old doctor, in her entertaining *Memoirs of Dr. Erasmus Darwin,* describes him amid his circle of Lichfield friends, which included Day of *Sanford and Merton* fame, and Richard Edgeworth, father of Maria Edgeworth, the cultured and attractive gentleman who married in rapid succession four ladies, each, it seems, undeterred by the fate of her predecessor worn out by excessive child bearing. The first Mrs. Darwin perished in the same conventional 18th century fashion, heaping encomiums, never-

theless, upon her husband. He was a caustic, sceptical, am-
orous, speculative man, who disapproved of spirituous liquors,
had advanced ideas upon diet, was highly successful as a
physician, though deemed by some too experimental, and who
pursued as his chief recreation the study of botany, with incidental excursions into all other sciences. He was likewise
interested in the arts and wrote verse, which he withheld
from publication until his practise as a physician should be
unshakably established.

   The Botanic Garden, (1791) Darwin's first long poem,
was popular in its day and ran through several editions. The
second part, *The Loves of the Plants,* was the theme of Canning's parody, *The Loves of the Triangles,* which had its
share in making the doctor's verse ridiculous to an age
cultivating a taste for romantic literature. Darwin's models
in verse, unlike his scientific speculations, were old-fashioned.
In an age which produced Cowper, Burns, and Blake he clung
to the heroic couplet, and his verse is imitative of the imitators
of Pope. To the modern ear it is unreadable as poetry. But
it nevertheless is highly entertaining for its content, its wealth
of scientific speculation, and in its conceptions is sometimes
sublime. The Doctor's imagination was scientific rather
than poetic. No more instructive object lesson as to what
constitutes poetry could be asked than a comparison of
Prometheus Unbound with *The Botanic Garden.* Yet in
both are ideas and images and concepts which are essentially
the same. Darwin was a scientist with the imaginative grasp
of a poet but almost wholly deficient in ear and in a sense
for the congruous associations of words and images. Shelley,
a poet endowed with those faculties which Darwin lacked,
had also greater powers of imagination and enough knowledge of science to grasp the implications of scientific theory.

   What Erasmus Darwin took it upon himself to do in

his scientific epics is evident in the "Advertisement" to the *Botanic Garden,* in which the author states:

The general design of the following sheets is to enlist Imagination under the banner of Science; and to lead her votaries from the looser analogies, which dress out the imagery of poetry, to the stricter ones, which form the ratiocination of philosophy. . . .

In the first Poem, or Economy of Vegetation, the physiology of Plants is delivered; and the operation of the Elements, as far as they may be supposed to affect the growth of Vegetables. In the second Poem, or Loves of the Plants, the Sexual System of Linneus is explained, with the remarkable properties of many particular plants.

An "Apology" follows of which the following excerpts are significant in their bearing upon Shelley:

It may be proper here to apologize for many of the subsequent conjectures on some articles of natural philosophy, as not being supported by accurate investigation or conclusive experiments. Extravagant theories however in those parts of philosophy, where our knowledge is yet imperfect, are not without their use; as they encourage the execution of laborious experiments; or the investigation of ingenious deductions, to confirm or refute them. . . .

The Rosicrucian doctrine of Gnomes, Sylphs, Nymphs, and Salamanders was thought to afford a proper machinery for a Botanic poem; as it is probable, that they were originally the names of hieroglyphic figures representing the elements.

Many of the important operations of nature were shadowed or allegorized in the heathen mythology, as the first Cupid springing from the Egg of Night, the marriage of Cupid and Psyche, the Rape of Proserpine, the Congress of Jupiter and Juno, The Death and Resuscitation of Adonis, etc. many of which are ingeniously explained in the works of Bacon, Vol. V, p. 47. 4th Edit. London, 1778. The Egyptians were possessed of many discoveries in philosophy and chemistry before the invention of letters; these were then expressed in hieroglyphic paintings of men and animals; which after the discovery of the alphabet were described and animated by the poets and became first the deities of Egypt, and afterwards of Greece and Rome.

Darwin conceives the imagination essential to scientific speculation and thus gives rein to his. The machinery of sylphs and salamanders borrowed from Rosicrucian lore, probably at the inspiration of Pope's *Rape of the Lock,* is in Darwin's use wholly stiff and frigid. Yet it must have appealed to Shelley, already versed in occultism; for Shelley's personifications in *Prometheus,* though immensely more vital—his spirits of the Hours, Earth, and Moon, his Echoes and Spirits of the Human Mind—are creatures similar in kind. Shelley's use of the word genii to personify elemental forces, as in *Queen Mab* and *The Cloud*, may derive from Darwin's similar use, for an early note in *The Botanic Garden* upon the gnomes and nymphs states, "It is probable that they were originally the names of hieroglyphic figures of the Elements, or of Genii presiding over their operations."

The four books of the *Botanic Garden* are devoted to the chemical, physical, and biological activities of the personified forces of earth, air, fire, and water. The epic is a scientific primer in verse, and the notes which accompany it, whether as footnotes or in a larger appendix of Additional Notes, bulk larger than the text. In them are discussions of all imaginable scientific subjects, geological, botanical, astronomical, chemical, and electrical. And inasmuch as Darwin was evidently widely read in the scientific writing of the day the modern reader can, if he desires, by following Darwin's leads and utilizing the bibliographical references, soon become more or less acquainted with the science of the time.

To the reader unversed in eighteenth century science the range and extent of this literature and the boldness of many of its speculations come as a surprise. The latter half of the eighteenth century laid the basis of modern science in chemistry, astronomy, biology, geology, and electricity. The renascence of science which accompanied the renascence of literature is marked with as many and as great names, and its importance to the world of today is doubtless greater. That the fact is not more generally recognized is due to a lack of qualified historians, for science is more concerned with new discoveries than with tracing its own origins and development; and literary and cultural historians largely ignore its literature. Yet this literature is for the most part intelligible to any educated person. The elaborate technical terminology of our day had not yet been invented, and a knowledge of the higher mathematics is necessary only to an understanding of some parts of astronomy and physics. Though Shelley confessedly knew little mathematics it was therefore possible for him to keep abreast of the scientific advances of his time. Chemistry and electricity, the subjects in which he was most interested, were in their infancy. Speculation in these fields was daring and far-reaching, anticipating modern ideas to an extent surprising to the reader who investigates the scientific journals of the time. But the technical and detailed verification of hypotheses had only begun.

Though Shelley was a highly imaginative poet and thinker, his speculations, which bridge the gap between science and metaphysics, and which advance ideas that we think of as modern, had their basis in the scientific thought of his day. In his later development he is more the philosopher than the scientist. He seizes upon hypotheses as then unproved by experiment and utilizes them in his dream of a regenerate world. He seeks to reconcile science and metaphysics, materialism and mysticism. For his most finely spun imaginings there is yet usually some scientific justification. To assume of a line of Shelley's verse that beneath its highly wrought dress there is no hard core of intellectual meaning, is to miss almost inevitably its true significance. The degree to which Shelley was a scientist in the modern meaning of the term is difficult to decide. His actual experimentation seems to have been restricted to his earlier years before he devoted himself to reform and to have been limited to chemistry and electricity. But he evidently continued to be widely read in scientific philosophy and to the last found in it suggestion and inspiration for poetry.

Hence the importance of Darwin as suggesting to Shelley the poetic possibilities of scientific matter, and as opening his imagination to the far reaching speculations of scientific thought. Darwin, to be sure, exploited his science in a most unpoetical fashion, but Shelley, as has been remarked, was familiar with Lucretius, who had made good poetry from the scientific speculations of an earlier day. There were new wonders to tell of which Lucretius had not dreamed. If Darwin supplied new matter in a poetical garb of which Shelley could not assuredly approve, there was nothing to prevent a better poet, such as himself, from utilizing the same material. In Lucretius and Darwin is sufficient poetic precedent for *Prometheus Unbound,* beauty of form in the one, and solidity of scientific thought in the other.

Nor must Darwin have been the less attractive to Shelley for indulging in scientific imaginings which were deemed fanciful by more cautious minds. Time has shown some of these guesses to be not much amiss. Thus in the *Botanic Garden:*

"Soon shall thy arm, *Unconquer'd Steam!* afar
> Drag the slow barge, or drive the rapid car;
> Or on wide-waving wings expanded bear
> The flying-chariot through the fields of air.
> —Fair crews triumphant, leaning from above,
> Shall wave their fluttering kerchiefs as they move;
> Or warrior-bands alarm the gaping croud.
> And armies shrink beneath the shadowy cloud.
> > *Botanic Garden* I. ll. 289-296.

Two footnotes elucidate further:

There is reason to believe it [steam] may in time be applied to the rowing of barges, and the moving of carriages along the road. As the specific levity of air is too great for the support of great burthens by balloons there seems no probable method of flying conveniently but by the power of steam, or some other explosive material; which another half century may probably discover.

And again:

From the cheapness with which a very powerful gunpowder is likely soon to be manufactured from aerated marine acid, or from a new method of forming nitrous acid by means of manganese or other calciform ores, it may probably in time be applied to move machinery, and supersede the use of steam.

In Shelley the prophecy of aerial flight is thus briefly expressed:

> The tempest is his steed, he strides the air.
>
> *P. U.* IV. l. 421.

Tennyson's picture of the aerial navies grappling in the blue has often been remarked as evidence of his prophetic vision. In the lines previously cited, Darwin clearly anticipates him.

In other verses or in notes Darwin invokes the secret by which the winds are controlled. The winds, he thinks, have some chemical cause and will be mastered by chemical and electrical means. Climate might also be made more equable by towing icebergs from the polar to the tropical regions, a better use for the navies of the world, thinks Darwin, good eighteenth century anti-militarist, than fighting each other. Rainfall may, perhaps, be thus induced:

> *Nymphs!* o'er the soil ten thousand points erect,
> And high in air the electric flame collect.
> Soon shall dark mists with self-attraction shroud

The blazing day, and sail in wilds of cloud;
Each silvery Flower the streams aerial quaff,
Bow her sweet head, and infant Harvest laugh.
Botanic Garden, I. ll. 553-558.

A note elucidates:

The solution of water in air or in calorique, seems to acquire electric matter at the same time. . . . Hence it appears, that though clouds by their change of form may sometimes become electrified minus, yet they have in general an accumulation of electricity. This accumulation of electric matter also evidently contributes to support the atmospheric vapour when it is condensed into the form of clouds, because it is seen to descend rapidly after the flashes of lightning have diminished its quantity; whence there is reason to conclude that very numerous metallic rods with fine points erected high in the air might induce it at any time to part with some of its water.

Such speculations, reminiscent of Franklin, are character-istic. Darwin put imagination in service to science quite in the spirit of his own preachments. Were these, however, Dar-win's sole contribution to thought, they would be worthy only of passing notice. It is as a representative figure, as sci-entist and scientific philosopher, that Darwin is important to the Shelley student seeking a knowledge of the intellectual climate in which Shelley's mind matured. Darwin, no less than Locke, Hume, Voltaire, and Godwin is representative of the older order which, in Shelley's day, changed so rapidly. Probably in no other single figure—certainly in no other sci-entific figure—of the late eighteenth century can so wide and so representative a body of ideas be found. The philosophic and scientific world of 1775-1800 is mirrored in his verse and notes.

In sketching this intellectual world of Darwin, citation will be made from *The Botanic Garden* (1791), from the *Zoonomia* (1793-96), and from *The Temple of Nature* (1803), his last work, whose sub-title, *Or the Origin of Society,* indicates a scope somewhat greater than that of *The Botanic Garden*. The canto headings are: "Production of Life," "Reproduction of Life," "Progress of the Mind," and "Of Good and Evil." The first two cantos repeat many of the ideas previously set forth in *The Botanic Garden*. But the scientific notes display the author's latest readings and especially his matured views on the theme of evolution. Philosophically, also, its theme is wider. The author depicts not only the processes of nature but endeavors to find man's place therein. The initial invocation to Immortal Love, which indicates the poem's scope and theme, calls to mind passages in *Prometheus Unbound*:

> *Immortal Love!* who ere the morn of Time,
> On wings outstretch'd o'er chaos hung sublime,
> Warm'd into life the bursting egg of Night,
> And gave young Nature to admiring Light—
> *You!* whose wide arms, in soft embraces hurl'd
> Round the vast frame, connect the whirling world!
> Whether immers'd in day, the Sun your throne,
> You gird the planets in your silver zone;
> Or warm, descending on ethereal wing,
> The earth's cold bosom with the beams of spring;
> Press drop to drop, to atom atom bind,
> Link sex to sex, or rivet mind to mind;
> Attend my song!
>
> *Temple of Nature,* I. ll. 15-27.

Darwin blandly ignores religious controversy. Incidents from Biblical history embellish his pages quite as do incidents from classical mythology. Their purpose is decorative merely, and after a description of natural processes wholly evolutionary in character the reader comes upon a rosy passage depicting Adam and Eve in the Garden:

On sun-bright lawns unclad the Graces stray'd,
And guiltless Cupids haunted every glade;
Till the fair Bride, forbidden shades among,
Heard unalarm'd the Tempter's serpent-tongue;
Eyed the sweet fruit, the mandate disobey'd,
And her fond Lord with sweeter smiles betray'd.
Conscious awhile with throbbing heart he strove,
Spread his wide arms, and barter'd life for love!

Temple of Nature, I. ll. 39-46.

Passages could be cited from Darwin to prove him a
Deist, a term of rather vague implications. He postulates
some first cause which may, by courtesy, be called God. But
it is the spirit in nature, the creative force in life, which, as
scientist, really concerns him. Shelley's Spirit of Nature,
which in *Queen Mab* so anomalously is revered whereas God
is fiercely denounced, is harmonious with Darwin's conception if not derivative from it. In *Prometheus* likewise the
Immortal Love of Darwin's invocation is the ruler of the
universe and, as in Darwin's philosophy, identifiable with
the physical attractive forces in nature—cohesion, gravitation,
electricity and magnetism.

How great is Darwin's share in shaping Shelley's philosophical ideas is indeterminable. I shall later have occasion to
cite passages from *Prometheus* together with parallels from
Darwin. In these the indebtedness is clear. Larger philosophical analogies may only be pointed out and the question of indebtedness remain speculative. For Darwin's philosophy is
in itself derivative, has its long and complicated history, and
with its sources Shelley was independently familiar. It is
indeed of no particular importance that one should determine
of a passage in Shelley, "This derives unmistakably from a
certain book." All that is essential is to discover contemporary
and antecedent ideas which make Shelley more intelligible.

There need be no question of Shelley's originality, but like all poets and thinkers he is the product of his age, an inheritor of the past; knowledge of that past is necessary to an understanding of him.

Darwin's basic concepts of matter and its motions may thus be briefly summarized from the *Zoonomia:*

All Nature consists of two essences:

1. Spirit, power to produce motion.
2. Matter, to receive and communicate motion.

Primary motions divided into three classes, to which he supposes the fourth should be added:

1. Gravitation: rotation of earth and planets, flux of ocean, descent of bodies;
2. Chemical: many of these facts are "nicely ascertained and elegantly classed";
3. Life: all motions of animal and vegetable world, blood vessels, muscles, organs of sense.
4. Supposed ethereal fluids of magnetism, electricity, heat, light.[2]

Allusion to the immaterial philosophies of Plato and Berkeley is evident in another passage:

Some, who have espoused the doctrine of the immateriality of ideas, have seriously doubted the existence of a material world, with which only our senses acquaint us; and yet have assented to the existence of spirit, with which our senses cannot acquaint us; and have finally allowed, that all our knowledge is derived through the medium of our senses! They forget, that if the spirit of animation had no properties in common with matter, it could neither affect nor be affected by the material body.[3]

In *Prometheus,* identity of matter and spirit is apparent, a thesis derivable alike from Plato and from Newton. Darwin is not clear and explicit on this point, though occasional

[2] *Zoonomia*, I, 5-6. (2 ed. London, 1796).
[3] *Ibid.*, II, 635.

passages point to his nominal acceptance of an immaterial philosophy, as in his description of the "Nymphs," personifications of the forces of air:

> Forms sphered in fire with trembling light array'd,
> Ens without weight, and substance without shade;
> *Botanic Garden*, I. ll. 423-4.

Herein, energy is represented as without material substance, a theme to which the discussion will subsequently recur in the consideration of Newton and Davy. Another note from the *Botanic Garden* noncommittally cites the old philosophers to this effect:

The perpetual circulation of matter in the growth and dissolution of vegetable and animal bodies seems to have given Pythagoras his idea of the metempsycosis or transmigration of spirit; which was afterwards dressed out or ridiculed in a variety of amusing fables. Other philosophers have supposed that there are two different materials or essences, which fill the universe. One of these, which has the power of commencing or producing motion, is called spirit; the other which has the power of receiving and of communicating motion, but not of beginning it, is called matter. The former of these is supposed to be diffused through all space, filling up the interstices of the suns and planets, and constituting the gravitations of the sidereal bodies, the attractions of chemistry, with the spirit of vegetation, and of animation. The latter occupies but comparatively small space, constituting the solid parts of the suns and planets, and their atmospheres. Hence these philosophers have supposed, that both matter and spirit are equally immortal and unperishable; and that on the dissolution of vegetable or animal organization, the matter returns to the general mass of matter; and the spirit to the general mass of spirit, to enter again into new combinations, according to the original idea of Pythagoras.[4]

The cosmic universe of Darwin's conception is the universe of Newton and Herschel:

[4] *Botanic Garden*, note to l. 574, Canto II.

"Let there be Light!" proclaim'd the *Almighty* Lord,
Astonish'd Chaos heard the potent word;—
Through all his realms the kindling Ether runs,
And the mass starts into a million suns;
Earths round each sun with quick explosions burst,
And second planets issue from the first;
Bend, as they journey with projectile force,
In bright ellipses their reluctant course,
Orbs wheel in orbs, round centres centres roll,
And form, self-balanced, one revolving Whole.
                    Botanic Garden, I. ll. 103-112.

In a note to this passage Darwin states:

Mr. Herschel has given a very sublime and curious account of the construction of the heavens with his discovery of some thousand nebulae, or clouds of stars; many of which are much larger collections of stars, than all those put together, which are visible to our naked eyes, added to those which form the galaxy, or milky zone, which surrounds us. He observes that in the vicinity of these clusters of stars there are proportionally fewer stars than in other parts of the heavens, and hence he concludes, that they have attracted each other, on the supposition that infinite space was at first equally sprinkled with them; as if it had at the beginning been filled with a fluid mass, which had coagulated. Mr. Herschel has further shown, that the whole sidereal system is gradually moving round some centre, which may be an opake mass of matter, Philos. Trans. Vol. LXXIV. . . .

If these innumerable and immense suns thus rising out of chaos are supposed to have thrown out their attendant planets by new explosions, as they ascended; and those their respective satellites, filling in a moment the immensity of space with light and motion, a grander idea cannot be conceived by the mind of man.

The extinction of the stellar universe Darwin, in conformity with this thesis, thus depicts:

Star after star from Heaven's high arch shall rush,
Suns sink on suns, and systems systems crush
Headlong, extinct, to one dark centre fall,

And Death and Night and Chaos mingle all!
—Till o'er the wreck, emerging from the storm,
Immortal *Nature* lifts her changeful form,
Mounts from her funeral pyre on wings of flame,
And soars and shines, another and the same.

Botanic Garden, IV. ll. 373-380.

How, specifically, Nature is to emerge from death and night, is somewhat vaguely stated in a note depicting the final destruction and rebirth of the universe:

Thus all the suns, and the planets, which circle round them, may again sink into one central chaos; and may again by explosions produce a new world; which in process of time may resemble the present one, and at length again undergo the same catastrophe! these great events may be the result of the immutable laws impressed on matter by the Great Cause of Causes, Parent of Parents, Ens Entium![5]

In the light of the present day theories of the atom and its part in the cyclical history of the stars, Darwin's use of the word 'explosion' is a surmise uncannily shrewd, but I do not know upon what it is based.

Shelley, in Demogorgon's last speech in *Prometheus,* envisages a similar catastrophe.

. . . if, with infirm hand, Eternity,
Mother of many acts and hours, should free
The serpent that would clasp her with his length.

To him the "spells" wherewith the universe is to be restored are

Gentleness, Virtue, Wisdom, and Endurance.

This is scientifically even less specific than Darwin's statement unless it be supposed that these qualities are constituents of the Love that

folds over the world its healing wings.

[5] *Temple of Nature,* note pp. 166-167.

Love, in Shelley's employment of the word in *Prometheus,* is both a spiritual and a physical power, in the latter sense identifiable with electricity. But of this more in a subsequent chapter.

Darwin's astronomical allusions are largely incidental to scientific matter closer to his interest. One passage descriptive of the moon and a note accompanying it are, however, important as perhaps suggesting to Shelley the idea of frozen oceans in the moon and the possibility of the moon's becoming habitable, a theme which is celebrated in the description of the Promethean age in *Prometheus Unbound:*

> *Gnomes!* how you gazed, when from her wounded side
> Where now the South-Sea heaves its waste of tide,
> Rose on swift wheels the *Moon's* refulgent car,
> Circling the solar orb, a sister star,
> Dimpled with vales, with shining hills emboss'd,
> And roll'd round Earth her airless realms of frost.
>
> *Botanic Garden,* II. ll. 77-82.

The reference is to the old belief that the moon was torn from that side of the earth now filled with the Pacific Ocean. Darwin adds a further note.

If the moon had no atmosphere at the time of its elevation from the earth; or if its atmosphere was afterwards stolen from it by the earth's attraction; the water on the moon would rise quickly into vapour; and the cold produced by a certain quantity of this evaporation would congeal the remainder of it. Hence it is not probable that the moon is at present inhabited, but as it seems to have suffered and to continue to suffer much by volcanoes, a sufficient quantity of air may in process of time be generated to produce an atmosphere; which may prevent its heat from so easily escaping, and its water from so easily evaporating, and thence become fit for the production of vegetables and animals.

That the moon possesses little or no atmosphere is deduced

from the undiminished lustre of the stars, at the instant when they emerge from behind her disk. That the ocean of the moon is frozen, is confirmed from there being no appearance of lunar tides; which, if they existed, would cover the part of her disk nearest the earth.

The present activity of solar volcanoes is a reference to the supposed discovery by Herschel of live volcanoes on the moon. In his "Additional Notes" to the *Botanic Garden* Darwin cites Herschel as "having discovered a volcanic crater three miles broad burning on her disk."

Pursuant of one of his favorite theses that the figures of ancient mythology are symbols of scientific facts known to the priestly caste of Egypt and Greece, Darwin interprets Venus as the personification of life rising from the sea.

The Egyptian figure of Venus rising from the sea seems to have represented the Beauty of organic Nature; which the philosophers of that country, the magi, appear to have discovered to have been elevated by earth-quake from the primeval ocean. But the hieroglyphic figure of Adonis seems to have signified the spirit of animation or life, which was perpetually wooed or courted by organic matter, and which perished and revived alternately.[6]

The theory that the earth was once covered with water and that the earliest forms of life were in the sea is as old as Thales. Venus, personifying life and love and earthly beauty, is appropriately therefore sea-born. Asia in *Prometheus Unbound* seemingly is no other than this earthly Venus, to which conception Shelley adds, characteristically, Platonic implications. The science of Darwin's and Shelley's time had, however, endowed the ancient fable with new and specific meanings both geological and zoölogical. Important chiefly, and essential to the evolutionary thesis of the slow modification of life forms, is the perception that vast periods of time

[6] *Temple of Nature,* 47.

are necessary to account for the earth's history, a belief countenanced by the newer astronomical ideas of stellar evolution. Darwin repeatedly stresses the vast age of the primeval
world.

From the increased knowledge in Geology during the present
century, owing to the greater attention of philosophers to the situations of the different materials, which compose the strata of the
earth, as well as to their chemical properties, it seems clearly to
appear, that the nucleus of the globe beneath the ocean consisted
of granite; and that on this the great beds of limestone were
formed from the shells of marine animals during the innumerable
primeval ages of the world; and that whatever strata lie on these
beds of limestone, or on the granite, where the limestone does not
cover it, were formed after the elevation of islands and continents
above the surface of the sea by the recrements of vegetables and of
terrestrial animals.[7]

and again:

The perpetual production and increase of the strata of limestone from the shells of aquatic animals; and of all those incum-
bent on them from the recrements of vegetables and of terrestrial
animals, are now well understood from our improved knowledge
of geology; and show, that the solid parts of the globe are gradually enlarging, and consequently that it is young; as the fluid parts
are not yet all converted into solid ones. Add to this, that some
parts of the earth and its inhabitants appear younger than others—
etc.[8]

The explanation, astronomical and geological, of an early
aquatic world Darwin derives from a *Treatise on the Theory
of the Earth* by Whitehurst "a watchmaker and engineer at
Derby, but whose ingenuity, integrity, and humanity, were
rarely equalled in any station of life." The comment has interest as indicating the universality of scientific curiosity in the

[7] *Ibid.*, note p. 164.
[8] *Ibid.*, note p. 19.

late eighteenth century and the part played by amateurs in scientific speculation and experiment. The articles in the scientific magazines and especially the correspondence of readers attest the fact. Doctors, engineers, gentlemen of leisure might reasonably aspire in those happy days to make genuine contributions to sciences yet in their infancy. Darwin's note summarizes Whitehurst's theory thus:

If the nucleus of the earth was thrown out from the sun by an explosion along with as large a quantity of surrounding hot vapour as its attraction would occasion to accompany it, the ponderous semi-fluid nucleus would take a spherical form from the attraction of its own parts, which would become an oblate spheroid from its diurnal revolution. As the vapour cooled, the water would be precipitated, and an ocean would surround the spherical nucleus with a superincumbent atmosphere. The nucleus of solar lava would likewise become harder as it became cooler.[9]

Darwin devotes many lines of verse and copious notes to the details of the formation of strata and of chalk, marble, granite, the minerals, and acids.

> So, fold on fold, Earth's wavy plains extend
> And, sphere in sphere, its hidden strata bend.
>
> *Botanic Garden,* IV. ll. 401-2.

The discussion of metals leads him to one of his speculations prescient of modern science:

The transmutation of one metal into another, though hitherto undiscovered by the alchymists, does not appear impossible; such transmutations have been supposed to exist in nature. . . . So silver is found mixed in almost all lead-ores, and sometimes in separate filaments within the cavities of lead-ore . . . and is thence probably a partial transmutation of the lead to silver, the rapid progress of modern chemistry having shown the analogy between the metallic calces and acids, may lead to the power of transmuting their bases: a discovery much to be wished.[10]

[9] *Botanic Garden,* note to l. 17, Canto II.
[10] *Ibid.,* to l. 398, Canto II.

Great heat is essential to such transmutations. Darwin alludes to the theory that the center of the earth is molten:

Many philosophers have believed that the central parts of the earth consist of a fluid mass of burning lava, which they have called a subterranean sun, and have supposed that it contributes to the production of metals, and to the growth of vegetables.[11]

From cracks and fissures leading to the central burning mass, steam arises forming hot springs.

And up these cracks I suppose certain vapours arise, which either alone, or by meeting with something descending into them from above, have produced most of the metals; and several of the materials in which they are bedded.[12]

In other passages, however, it is evident that Darwin inclines rather to the belief that the core of the earth is not molten and that the volcanic fires are in wells or pockets.

Volcanoes Darwin supposes to have been caused by seawater pouring into the burning caverns of the earth with resultant steam and explosions. And he considers the possibility of other vapors even more expansive as thus created. To volcanic origin he attributes "medicated streams" as at Buxton, and to volcanic eruptions "contagious atoms" which are the source of pestilence.

Those epidemic complaints, which are generally termed influenza, are believed to arise from vapours thrown out from earthquakes in such abundance as to affect large regions of the atmosphere.[13]

It is a passage to recall in connection with the Earth's lament in *Prometheus*

[11] *Ibid.*, note to l. 139, Canto I.
[12] *Ibid.*, note to l. 398, Canto II.
[13] *Temple of Nature*, note p. 140.

And birds, and beasts, and fish, and human shapes,
Which drew disease and pain from my wan bosom,
Draining the poison of despair. . . .
                                    P. U. III. 3, ll. 93-95.

In Darwin's picture of the world of nature, the atmosphere, formation of gases, rainfall, and attendant meteorological phenomena occupy perhaps the most important place, an emphasis explicable in one who was foremost a botanist. The complexity of the subject makes it difficult to present in simple outline, for the forces of heat, electricity, and magnetism are involved with the life processes of animals and plants, and the phenomena incidentally encountered range from the renovation of the atmosphere to the Aurora Borealis. Priestley's analysis of the constituents of the air and certain gases, Lavoisier's determination of the nature of water, and the wide interest and experimentation in electricity and meteorological phenomena contribute to the explanation of that round of creation, destruction, and renovation in which clouds, heat, rain, gases, the growth and destruction of plants and animals, and the activities of electricity all play a part.

Heat he conceives to be an etherial fluid, the direct opposite in its action to the force of gravitation:

The matter of heat is an ethereal fluid, in which all things are immersed, and which constitutes the general power of repulsion; as appears in explosions which are produced by the sudden evolution of combined heat; and by the expansion of all bodies by the slower diffusion of it in its uncombined state. Without heat all the matter of the world would be condensed into a point by the power of attraction; and neither fluidity nor life could exist. There are also particular powers of repulsion, as those of magnetism and electricity, and of chemistry, such as oil and water; which last may be as numerous as the particular attractions which constitute chemical affinities; and may both of them exist as atmospheres round the individual particles of matter.[14]

[14] *Temple of Nature,* note p. 20.

Again in the *Zoonomia* he identifies heat and motion:

Without heat and motion, which some philosophers still believe to be the same thing, as they so perpetually appear together, the particles of matter would attract and move towards each other, and the whole universe freeze or coalesce into one solid mass. These therefore counteract the gravitation of bodies to one center; and not only prevent the planets from falling into the sun, but become either the efficient causes of vegetable and animal life, or the causes without which life cannot exist; as by their means the component particles of matter are enabled to slide over each other with all the various degrees of fluidity and repulsion.[15]

Light he conceives to be "essentially different from heat," basing his conclusion upon his study of the effects of light upon plants. Without light plants become "blanched or etiolated." The upper surface of leaves, which Darwin conceives to be their organ of respiration, "seem to require light as well as air." The "perspirable matter" given off through the pores of the plant is acted upon by the sun's light and "appears to be decomposed."

. . . the hydrogene becomes a part of the vegetable, composing oils or resins: and the oxygene combined with light or calorique ascends, producing the pure part of the atmosphere or vital air. Hence during the light of the day vegetables give up more pure air than their respiration injures; but not so in the night, even though equally exposed to warmth. This single fact would seem to show that light is essentially different from heat.[16]

In the "laboratory of nature"—Darwin's term—there is, then, a perpetual round of chemical reactions whereby vegetation is nourished and the air replenished. Oxygen and hydrogen are liberated for the renewal of the atmosphere and the formation of water, and nitrogen, or azote as it was then called, supplies food for plant life. It was the chemical studies

[15] *Zoonomia*, II, 511.
[16] *Botanic Garden*, note to l. 462, Canto I.

of the time, the discovery and isolation of the elements, which permitted this glimpse into nature's processes. The precise technique of the complex series of phenomena is a theme for varied speculation. Thus:

> It is probable that on a sunny morning much pure air becomes separated from the dew by means of the points of vegetables on which it adheres, and much inflammable air [hydrogen] imbibed by the vegetable, or combined with it; and by the sun's light thus decomposing water the effects of it in bleaching linen seems to depend.[17]

Darwin's "Additional Notes" with their extensive discussions of various botanical problems go more fully into this question of the relation of plant life to the renovation of the atmosphere and to the cyclical history of the elements oxygen, hydrogen, and nitrogen. The recent discoveries of Priestley and Lavoisier in determining the constitution of air and water and in isolating their elements had tremendously widened the knowledge of plant life and of meteorology and, especially, of their interdependence. These phenomena are a theme both of Darwin's verse and of elaborate annotation. In *Prometheus Unbound* the dialogue of the Fauns is, as will be seen, to be interpreted in the light of Darwin's precedent practise and notes. It is evident that the formation of gases in nature, their part in the growth of plants and animals, and their relation to atmospheric electricity are important in Shelley's interpretation of the physical universe. The emphasis is a natural one in view both of Darwin's prior employment of them in verse and of their intrinsic significance. Especially they serve as a vital link between animate and inanimate nature.

Vital as are all three, hydrogen, oxygen, and nitrogen, to life, it is hydrogen which, by reason of its lightness, provokes

[17] *Botanic Garden,* additional note XXXIV.

the most extensive and interesting speculation. It has been shown by Cavendish, Darwin writes, "that the gas called inflammable air is at least ten times lighter than common air; Mr. Lavoisier contends, that it is one of the component parts of water, and is by him called hydrogene. It is supposed to afford their principal nourishment to vegetables and thence to animals, and is perpetually arising from their decomposition."[18] This liberated hydrogen formed, it was supposed, a super-aerial atmosphere of great tenuity with various attendant phenomena, chief among which are those of an electrical nature:

> Between the termination of the aerial and the beginning of the gaseous atmosphere, the airs will occasionally be intermixed, and thus become inflammable by the electric spark; these circumstances will assist in explaining the phenomena of fire balls, northern lights, and of some variable winds, and long-continued rains.[19]

Numerous notes and, in especial, Note I of the "Additional Notes" to the *Botanic Garden* elaborate upon the electric phenomena of the upper and lower atmosphere. In the lower region of dense air "common lightning is produced from the accumulation or defect of electric matter in those floating fields of vapour in respect to each other, or in respect to the earth beneath them, or the dissolved vapour above them, which is constantly varying both with the change of the form of the clouds, which thus evolve a greater or less surface, and also with their ever-changing degree of condensation." In the second region of the atmosphere, too tenuous to support clouds, there is yet "invisible vapour, or water in aerial solution." It is "in this stratum it seems probable that the meteors called shooting stars are produced; and that they consist of electric

[18] *Ibid.*, note to l. 123, Canto I.
[19] *Ibid.*

sparks, or lightning, passing from one region to another of
these invisible fields of aero-aqueous solution."

The place of these shooting stars is apparently lower than
that of fireballs, which exist in the third stratum of the atmosphere, that of "inflammable gas" or hydrogen. These fire-
balls are sometimes estimated to be a mile and a half in cir-
cumference. They, too, in Darwin's terminology are "meteors." In character they differ from shooting stars in that
they are of greater size, travel at a far greater speed, throw off
sparks in their passage, and change color "from bright blue
to dusky red." "They differ from the northern lights in not
being diffused." Darwin considers them to be balls of electricity and the different colors which they exhibit as due to
the varying densities of the atmosphere through which they
pass. "What is there in nature can attract them at so great
a distance as 1000 miles, and so forcibly as to detach an electric spark of a mile diameter? Can volcanoes at the time of
their eruptions have this effect, as they are generally attended
with lightning?"[20]

Darwin surmises that it may be "electric streams which
constitute" the "northern lights." They "seem to be repelled
or radiated from an accumulation of that fluid in the north,
and not attracted like the fire-balls. . . . Their variety of colors
and the permanency of them, and even the breadth of them
in different places, may depend on their setting on fire the
mixture of inflammable and common air through which they
pass." Darwin then proceeds to consider Franklin's theory of
the phenomenon and concludes by suggesting a wholly different hypothesis of his own to the effect that "these northern
lights may be produced by the union of inflammable with
common air, without the assistance of the electric spark to

[20] A passage suggestive of a line in *Prometheus Unbound* "Like a volcano's
meteor-breathing chasm."   Act II, 3, l. 3.

throw them into combustion." The various solutions of the problem are clearly conjectural, but the general emphasis is upon electricity as the probable cause of all meteoric phenomena including the aurora borealis. The problem of the aurora will reappear when we take up a most interesting passage in *Prometheus*.

Nothing is alien to Darwin's scientific interest, but his conclusions with regard to clouds are somewhat better substantiated than those relating to the aurora borealis. Recent experiments, not only the classic experiment of Franklin in drawing lightning from the clouds, but those of Lavoisier and others had demonstrated the electrical character of clouds. "The solution of water in air or in calorique, seems to acquire electric matter at the same time, as appears from an experiment of Mr. Bennet." And, "If we may trust the theory of Mr. Lavoisier concerning the composition and decomposition of water, there would seem another source of thunder showers; and that is, that the two gases termed oxygene gas or vital air, and hydrogene gas or inflammable air, may exist in the summer atmosphere in a state of mixture but not of combination, and that the electric spark or flash of lightning may combine them and produce water instantaneously." If it is electrically charged water particles that constitute clouds "this accumulation of electric matter also evidently contributes to support the atmospheric vapour when it is condensed into the form of clouds, because it is seen to descend rapidly after the flashes of lightning have diminished its quantity."[21]

There is no need to dwell further here upon this aspect of meteorology, for atmospheric electricity and its attendant phenomena will be more fully discussed in another place. It suffices to indicate the importance of clouds and rainfall in the cycle of organic growth and decay, an importance of which

[21] *Botanic Garden*, note to l. 553, Canto I.

Darwin is fully aware. Numerous passages in his verse, together with his notes thereon, attest the fact.

I wish to enumerate some of the other phenomena attributed by Darwin to electricity and to quote briefly his speculations upon the nature of electricity and magnetism.

Electrical action is said to accompany the eruption of volcanoes and also to be one manifestation of the whirlwind—an association to be remarked in lines of *Prometheus*. There are several allusions to the electrical phenomena of the whirlwind.

In the West Indies the sea rises like a cone in the whirl, and is met by black clouds . . . the upper and lower airs exchange their plus or minus electricity in perpetual lightnings.[22]

The fairy rings of grass more luxuriant and richly green than the blades around are attributed to the lightning flash which calcines the soil at the edges of its cone-shaped discharge.[23]

Several notes reveal the extensive experimentation carried on in Darwin's time to determine the influence of electricity in forwarding the germination of plants. He alludes to Mr. Ingenhouz, who "did not succeed in his experiments, and thence doubts the success of those of others," and to M. Rouland who, like Ingenhouz, had formerly believed in the idea but whose experiments had produced negative results. On the other hand "Mr. D'Ormoy and the two Roziers have found the same success in numerous experiments which they have made in the last two years; and Mr. Carmoy has shown in a convincing manner that electricity accelerates germination." Darwin concludes that "the influence of electricity in forwarding the germination of plants and their growth seems to be pretty well established."[24]

[22] *Botanic Garden*, Additional Note XXXIII.
[23] *Ibid.*, Additional Note XIII.
[24] *Ibid.*, note to l. 463, Canto I.

In the *Zoonomia*, Darwin's large work on medicine, reference is made to current experiments conducted by Galvani, Volta, and others "to show a similitude between the spirit of animation and the electric fluid."[25]   These experiments Darwin deems inconclusive.   In another passage an analogous theory is discussed:

The similarity of the texture of the brain to that of the pancreas, and some other glands of the body, has induced the enquirers into this subject to believe, *that a fluid, perhaps much more subtle than the electric* aura, is separated from the blood by that organ for the purposes of motion and sensation.   When we recollect, that the electric fluid itself is actually accumulated and given out voluntarily by the torpedo and the gymnotus electricus . . . and lastly that it needs no perceptible tubes to convey it, this opinion seems not without probability.[26]

In the *Botanic Garden,* describing the effect of air upon the blood in producing animal heat, Darwin opines that there is another source in the "chemical combinations produced in all the glands" and adds:

Besides this there would seem to be another material received from the air by respiration; which is so necessary to life, that the embryon must learn to breathe almost within a minute after its birth, or it dies.   The perpetual necessity of breathing shews, that the material thus acquired is perpetually consuming or escaping, and on that account requires perpetual renovation.   Perhaps the spirit of animation itself is thus acquired from the atmosphere, which if it be supposed to be finer or more subtle than the electric matter, could not long be retained in our bodies, and must therefore require perpetual renovation.[27]

The science of Darwin's day was much concerned, both experimentally and speculatively, with the nature of elec-

[25] *Zoonomia*, II, 66.
[26] *Ibid.*, I, 10.
[27] *Botanic Garden*, note to l. 401, Canto I.

tricity and magnetism and their relationship to light and heat. They are characterized as fluids and are supposed to be of a twofold character, positive and negative, or in the case of electricity vitreous and resinous. Gravity and heat, also thought of as fluids, are antithetical in like fashion, the one contractile, the other expansive in its effect. In Additional Note XII of the *Temple of Nature* Darwin discusses the relationship of these forces and while admitting the imperfect state of our knowledge regarding them, points out their complementary nature: "if the power of attraction should cease to act, all matter would be dissipated by the power of repulsion into boundless space; and if heat, or the power of repulsion, should cease to act, the whole world would become one solid mass. . . ."

Magnetism, he believes, "coincides with electricity in so many important points, that the existence of two magnetic ethers, as well as of two electric ones, becomes highly probable." They are alike, he remarks, in that both originate from the earth and that the arctic "ether" is at one pole of the magnet and the antarctic at the other. In another passage he seems prophetic of Davy's subsequent speculations as to the nature of matter, speculations which anticipate modern theories so strikingly:

It is probable that this theory of electric and magnetic attractions and repulsions, which so visibly exist in atmospheres round larger masses of matter, may be applied to explain the invisible attractions and repulsions of the minute particles of bodies in chemical combinations and decompositions.

Though this review of Darwin's general scientific ideas exclusive of those upon the evolution of life forms, which is the subject of the next chapter, will seem to the reader more than sufficiently long, it is in reality but a part of the whole. I have endeavored to indicate the range of Darwin's interests, to show how fully he expresses the scientific curiosity of his day, and thus how stimulating his works must have been to the curious mind of Shelley. Darwin is one of the most imaginative of scientists. He believed in the experimental value of the daring hypothesis. Aside from Shelley's specific indebtedness to him as evidenced in passages later to be cited from *Prometheus,* there is a large general obligation which may rather be felt than particularized. Certain general resemblances it will, however, be profitable to sum up before taking up Darwin's contributions to the theory of evolution.

First is Darwin's use of scientific lore as the material of poetry, a use similar to that of Lucretius for whose work Shelley had a youthful admiration. Darwin, too, while not deeply versed in the ancient and modern philosophies, is not ignorant of them, and the bent of his mind is philosophic; he is not content with the discovery of unrelated scientific facts, nor even with the whole of biological knowledge. He wishes to understand the whole of nature. Shelley, in *Prometheus Unbound,* was similarly seeking a synthesis of science and metaphysics, endeavoring to reconcile materialism and mysticism. For this purpose Darwin furnished some of the materials, supplying speculations which, if unproved scientifically, were, nevertheless, provocative to one less concerned with scientific certainty than with philosophic plausibility.

There is, further, Darwin's reiterated belief that the ancient mythologies symbolize scientific lore—chemical mainly, though in part biological. Also Darwin's use, perfunctory though it be, of the machinery of Rosicrucianism and the personification of the elements. Shelley's use of personifications in *Prometheus* and his animation of forces and substances usually thought of as inanimate, are analogous to Darwin's practise in his scientific epics.

Darwin's belief in a slow geological evolution and of a vast period of time requisite for its enactment; his acceptance of Herschel's picture of stellar evolution with its prophecy of the final extinction of all heat and movement; the important place accorded meteorological phenomena; the many references to electricity and magnetism; his interest in the phenomena of clouds; his speculations as to the relation of the spirit of animation to electricity and magnetism or to some ethereal fluid even more subtle—all these facts and theories have their echoes in *Prometheus*. Shelley, to be sure, had read other scientific writers than Darwin, nor need he have acquired his information necessarily from Darwin alone, but rather from Darwin's sources. Some of these sources are definitely identifiable, others by inference. There are, moreover, writers after Darwin, such as Davy, whose speculations are more advanced or which open up new ground. It will be the aim of subsequent chapters to discuss the most important of the writers other than Darwin who influenced Shelley's scientific ideas. Yet it is nevertheless true that the greater part of the scientific allusions in the *Prometheus* are explicable upon a careful reading of Darwin's epics and the *Zoonomia*.

CHAPTER IV

ERASMUS DARWIN: II. THEORY OF EVOLUTION

Henry Fairfield Osborn concedes Erasmus Darwin complete anticipation of the theory of evolution usually ascribed to Lamarck but clearly enunciated by Darwin some years prior to Lamarck's first publications on this theme.[1] If Lamarckian evolution is returning to repute, as seems to be the case, then Erasmus Darwin must vie with his grandson as the founder of modern evolutionary thought. Yet so to phrase his importance is misleading. Evolutionary thought goes back to a time prior to Aristotle and the hypothesis in one form or another persisted in philosophy until the eighteenth century scientists began to discover facts which elevated it from an hypothesis to a theory. It is for his citation of evidence in behalf of the evolution of plant and animal forms, for his unqualified acceptance of it as the scheme of the universe, and for his advancement of a theory to explain it that Erasmus Darwin is notable.

Darwin's explanation of the causes of evolution differs from that of Buffon, the noted naturalist and his contemporary, in that he does not lay much stress upon modifications in plants and animals induced by the direct action of environment:

He believed that modifications spring from within by the reactions of the organism; thus he fully anticipated what is now known as the Lamarckian theory, and extended it even further than Lamarck, since he endowed plants with sensibility and attributed their evolution to their own efforts towards the attainment of certain structures.[2]

[1] *From the Greeks to Darwin, An Outline of the Development of the Evolution Idea*, by Henry Fairfield Osborn, New York, 1908.
[2] Osborn, 143.

Darwin was evidently familiar with Buffon's work, which he cites. His original observations are drawn largely from botany and human physiology and to some extent from birds and animals.

Scientific thought in the late eighteenth century was evolutionary in its character to a degree of which the modern reader, unless versed in the history of some science, is usually unaware. The thought of the age in all its chief manifestations was antagonistic to traditional religion. The acute conflict between the special creationists and the evolutionists did not, it is true, develop until later when religious life had been revivified and when the growing authority of science was feared by religious leaders. It was then perceived that the evolutionary ideas long current constituted a threat to the old form of belief. With the publication of *The Origin of Species* the conflict came to a head. By this time Erasmus Darwin's contributions were largely forgotten and Charles Darwin, while acknowledging indebtedness to his grandfather, differed from him wholly in his explanation of the causes underlying evolutionary phenomena, attacking the Lamarckian thesis with some bitterness.

A brief synopsis of Erasmus Darwin's evolutionary ideas will, then, reveal the character of the scientific philosophy in which Shelley grew up. That Shelley had read Lamarck is not evident, nor is the point of any importance in view of his familiarity with Darwin, in whose thought, as has been said, the Lamarckian theory is anticipated.

Venus, in the Greek mythology, symbolizes the beauty of organic Nature, which, says Darwin, was believed by the Magi "to have been elevated by earthquakes from the primeval ocean." But the "hieroglyphic figure of Adonis seems to have signified the spirit of animation or life, which was perpetually wooed or courted by organic matter, and which perished and revived alternately. Afterwards the fable of Adonis seems to have given origin to the first religion promising a resurrection from the dead."[3]

> *Organic Life* beneath the shoreless waves
> Was born and nurs'd in Ocean's pearly caves;
> First forms minute, unseen by spheric glass,
> Move on the mud, or pierce the watery mass;
> These, as successive generations bloom,
> New powers acquire, and larger limbs assume;
> Whence countless groups of vegetables spring,
> And breathing realms of fin, and feet, and wing.
>   *Temple of Nature,* I. ll. 295-302.

Darwin subscribes to the ancient Greek theory of the ultimate origins of life:

> Hence without parent by spontaneous birth
> Rise the first specks of animated earth;
> From Nature's womb the plant or insect swims,
> And buds or breathes, with microscopic limbs.
>   *Temple of Nature,* I. ll. 247-250.

In his copious notes to all such passages as these Darwin points out from the evidences of geology and the presence of shells in strata of the highest mountains that the earth must once have been covered with water and that, therefore, life must have begun in the sea. What thereafter ensues is set forth briefly in the following citation which summarizes the evolutionary process.

After islands or continents were raised above the primeval ocean, great numbers of the most simple animals would attempt to seek food at the edges or shores of the new land, and might thence gradually become amphibious; as is now seen in the frog, who changes from an aquatic animal to an amphibious one; and in the gnat, which changes from a natant to a volant state.

At the same time new microscopic animalcules would immedi-

[3] *Temple of Nature,* 47.

ately commence wherever there was warmth and moisture, and some organic matter, that might induce putridity. Those situated on dry land, and immersed in dry air, may gradually acquire new powers to preserve their existence; and by innumerable successive reproductions for some thousands, or perhaps millions of ages, may at length have produced many of the vegetable and animal inhabitants which now people the earth.

As innumerable shell-fish must have existed a long time beneath the ocean, before the calcareous mountains were produced and elevated; it is also probable, that many of the insect tribes, or less complicate animals, existed long before the quadrupeds or more complicate ones. . . .[4]

Poetically phrased:

> Cold gills aquatic form respiring lungs,
> And sounds aerial flow from slimy tongues.
>   *Temple of Nature,* I. ll. 333-334.

Man, then, is derivative from an animal ancestry infinitely long. The embryo in the stages of its development recapitulates this past:

At the nativity of the child it deposits the placenta or gills, and by expanding its lungs acquires more plentiful oxygenation from the currents of air, which it must now continue perpetually to respire to the end of its life; as it now quits the liquid element, in which it was produced, and like the tadpole, when it changes into a frog, becomes an aerial animal.[5]

To pre-natal experience Darwin attributes certain differences between young animals and children as to the facility with which they learn to walk:

It has been deemed a surprising instance of instinct, that calves and chickens should be able to walk by a few efforts almost immediately after their nativity; whilst the human infant in those countries where he is not incumbered with clothes, as in India, is

[4] *Temple of Nature,* 30.
[5] *Zoonomia,* I, 532-533.

five or six months, and in our climate almost a twelve month, before he can safely stand upon his feet.

The struggles of all animals in the womb must resemble their mode of swimming, as by this kind of motion they can best change their attitude in water. But the swimming of the calf and chicken resembles their manner of walking, which they have thus in part acquired before their nativity, and hence accomplish it afterwards with very few efforts, whilst the swimming of the human creature resembles that of the frog, and totally differs from his mode of walking.[6]

Though the human species is not so acute in some of its senses as are the lower animals, man much surpasses all of them in the accuracy of his sense of touch. It is to the hand that man is indebted for his keener understanding and his mastery of the world:

It has been supposed by some, that mankind were formerly quadrupeds as well as hermaphrodites; and that some parts of the body are not yet so convenient to an erect attitude as to a horizontal one; as the fundus of the bladder in an erect posture is not exactly over the insertion of the urethra; whence it is seldom completely evacuated, and thus renders mankind more subject to the stone, than if he had preserved his horizontality; these philosophers, with Buffon and Helvetius, seem to imagine, that mankind arose from one family of monkeys on the banks of the Mediterranean; who accidentally had learned to use the adductor pollicis, or that strong muscle which constitutes the ball of the thumb, and draws the point of it to meet the points of the fingers; which common monkeys do not; and that this muscle gradually increased in size, strength, and activity, in successive generations; and by this improved use of the sense of touch, that monkeys acquired clear ideas, and gradually became men.

Perhaps all the productions of nature are in their progress to greater perfection! an idea countenanced by modern discoveries and deductions concerning the progressive formation of the solid

[6] *Ibid.*, I, 139.

parts of the terraqueous globe, and consonant to the dignity of the Creator of all things.[7]

Evidences "that mankind and quadrupeds were formerly in an hermaphrodite state, are first deduced from the present existence of breasts and nipples in all the males; which latter swell on titillation like those of the females, and which are said to contain a milky fluid at their birth; and it is affirmed, that some men have given milk to their children in desert countries, where the mother has perished; as the male pigeon is said to give a kind of milk from his stomach along with the regurgitated food, to the young doves. . . ."[8]

Primarily a botanist, Darwin draws many analogies between the organs of plants and animals. He believes that "the individuals of the vegetable world may be considered as inferior or less perfect animals." Certain vegetable organs resemble lungs, "those of aquatic plants the gills of fish." There are "close similarities also in the digestive and reproductive systems." He believes "that the anthers and stigmas are real animals, attached indeed to their parent tree like polypi or coral insects, but capable of spontaneous motion; that they are affected by the passion of love, and furnished with powers of reproducing their species."[9] He thinks that plants have organs of taste, vision, touch, and one "analogous to our sense of smell." Plants sleep and, Darwin believes, even dream. A surmise that insect life may have its origin from plants is thus cautiously phrased.

I am acquainted with a philosopher, who contemplating this subject thinks it not impossible, that the first insects were the anthers or stigmas of flowers; which had by some means loosed themselves from their parent plant, like the male flowers of Vallis-

[7] *Temple of Nature,* 54.
[8] *Ibid.,* 53.
[9] *Zoonomia,* I, 104-105.

neria; and that many other insects have gradually in long process of time been formed from these; some acquiring wings, others fins, and others claws, from their ceaseless efforts to procure their food, or to secure themselves from injury. He contends, that none of these changes are more incomprehensible than the transformation of tadpoles into frogs, and caterpillars into butterflies.[10]

An evolutionary development of life forms from the "microscopic ens" born beneath the waves has thus far been sketched, the close analogy of plants to animals indicated, and some of the instances of the perpetuation in higher forms of life of organs and parts acquired in a lower enumerated. From these evidences arises Darwin's query:

From thus meditating on the great similarity of the structure of the warm-blooded animals, and at the same time the great changes they undergo both before and after their nativity; and by considering in how minute a portion of time many of the changes of animals above described have been produced; would it be too bold to imagine, that in the great length of time, since the earth began to exist, perhaps millions of ages before the commencement of the history of mankind, would it be too bold to imagine, that all warm-blooded animals have arisen from one living filament, which THE GREAT FIRST CAUSE endued with animality, with the power of acquiring new parts, attended with new propensities, directed by irritations, sensations, volitions, and associations; and thus possessing the faculty of continuing to improve by its own inherent activity, and of delivering down those improvements by generation to its posterity, world without end![11]

Vegetable life he believes peopled earth and ocean long before the existence of animals. The plants, at first simple in form, developed in complexity and size with the contest for air and light. "Shall we conjecture," he asks, "that one and the same kind of living filaments is and has been the cause of

[10] *Botanic Garden*, Additional Note XXXIX.
[11] *Zoonomia*, I, 509.

all organic life?"[12]   He is led to accept this conclusion because of "the great similarity in structure which obtains in all
warm-blooded animals . . . from the mouse and bat to the
elephant and whale."   This filament "in its advance to maturity" has acquired fingers and a fine sense of touch in man,
in others, claws, talons, hoofs, wings, and feathers.[13]   These
differences in forms and qualities have arisen "from the different irritabilities and sensibilities, or voluntarities, or asso-
ciabilities, of this original living filament."[14]   And "the great
variety of species of animals, which now tenant the earth, may
have had their origin from the mixture of a few natural
orders."[15]

That the evolutionary hypothesis is a very old one Darwin
observes.   It "seems not to have been unknown to the ancient
philosophers.   Plato . . . was of opinion, that mankind with
all other animals were originally hermaphrodites during the
infancy of the world, and were in process of time separated
into male and female."[16]   To Hume, also, Darwin makes
acknowledgment:

The late Mr. David Hume, in his posthumous works, places
the powers of generation much above those of our boasted reason;
. . . he concludes that the world itself might have been generated,
rather than created; that is, it might have been gradually produced
from very small beginnings, increasing by the activity of its inherent principles, rather than by a sudden evolution of the whole
by the Almighty fire.—What a magnificent idea of the infinite
power of THE GREAT ARCHITECT! THE CAUSE OF
CAUSES! PARENT OF PARENTS! ENS ENTIUM!
For if we may compare infinities, it would seem to require a
greater infinity of power to cause the causes of effects, than to
cause the effects themselves.   This idea is analogous to the im-
proving excellence observable in every part of the creation; such

---

[12] *Zoonomia*, I, 511.
[13] *Ibid.*, I, 506.
[14] *Ibid.*, I, 502.
[15] *Ibid.*, I, 502.
[16] *Ibid.*, I, 512.

as in the progressive increase of the solid or habitable parts of the earth from water; and in the progressive increase of the wisdom and happiness of its inhabitants; and is consonant to the idea of our present situation being a state of probation, which by our exertions we may improve, and are consequently responsible for our actions.[17]

Darwin, it is evident, was of the French Revolutionary school of thought, a "perfectibilian," a believer in the infinite possibilities of man. It was while this philosophy was in the ascendant that evolutionary ideas in science, so evidently consonant with it, flourished. With the reaction of Napoleonic times and the eclipse of revolutionary doctrine, the scientific radicalism of Darwin and others suffered likewise. It is interesting to read in Rees's *Cyclopedia* of 1819, an excellent work, after a brief statement of Darwin's filament theory and the development of forms and of intelligence through irritability, this concluding judgment: "It would be useless to enter into a further examination of the *Zoonomia,* which has long ceased to be popular; those who wish to see a complete refutation of the sophisms contained in it will read with satisfaction, 'Observations on the Zoonomia of Dr. Darwin, by Thomas Brown, Esq.' published at Edinburgh in 8 vo. in 1798."[18]

Darwin's theories were, it is evident, of little repute when Shelley in 1818-19 was writing *Prometheus.* So, also, were all the radical ideas, humanitarian, social, and philosophical to which Shelley clung during the long period of reaction whose termination he did not live to see. Darwin's unpopularity would be for Shelley a claim to interest and credence. Moreover the influence of Darwin's evolutionary thought upon Shelley, so far as it is clearly discernible, is not in minor and strictly scientific details but in the larger philosophy of evolu-

[17] *Ibid.,* I, 513.
[18] Rees's *Cyclopedia,* article Erasmus Darwin.

tion, the theory of the cause to which the evolution of forms may be assigned. Here Shelley, as will be seen, is wholly in accord with Darwin.

Darwin believes, then, that the animals of "this terraqueous globe . . . have constantly improved, and are still in a state of progressive improvement." The "idea of the gradual generation of all things," was as Darwin points out, "as familiar to the ancient philosophers as to modern ones." The hieroglyphic figure of the first great egg, produced by night, and animated by Divine Love, expresses this belief in symbolical form. Love as the first cause and the ultimate power that triumphs over evil and the divinity of man's creation, Jupiter, is likewise dominant in Shelley's conception. That Shelley derives the idea wholly from Darwin is unlikely. But it is plausible that for Shelley Darwin's statement of it lent additional weight to the beliefs of the ancient philosophers. Science, as taught by a notable modern, seemed thus to be in harmony with neo-Platonism.

In the modern discoveries of chemistry, geology, and astronomy, as in biology, Darwin finds additional demonstration of a Deity, one who creates the atoms and the life filament, endows these with "certain immutable properties" through which they develop and thus creates the world as we see it, a world, evidently, which must run of itself according to its innate principles and without further divine interposition; a world, likewise, "which by our exertions we may improve, and are consequently responsible for our actions."

Unlike Shelley, Darwin had no wish to engage in controversy with theologians; he did not care to dispute about words. He is, he says, willing to allow "that the powers of gravity, specific attraction, electricity, magnetism, and even the spirit of animation, may consist of matter of a finer kind; and to believe with St. Paul and Malebranch, that the ultimate cause only of all motion is immaterial, that is God."[19]   And by the phrase "spirit of animation" he means "only that animal life which mankind possesses in common with brutes, and in some degree even with vegetables, and leave the consideration of the immortal part of us, which is the object of religion, to those who treat of revelation."   If, he concedes, the immaterial power of motion and material substance constitute the dualism of the world, the immaterial agent may be quite distinct from matter and capable of existence without it.   And thus, "the spirit of animation would appear to be capable of existing as well separately from the body as with it."

As to the way of evolution in life forms Darwin cites a number of interesting observations.   The means of procuring food "has diversified the forms of all species of animals.   Thus the nose of the swine has become hard for the purpose of turning up the soil in search of insects and of roots.   The trunk of the elephant is an elongation of the nose for the purpose of pulling down the branches of trees for his food, and for taking up water without bending his knees."   These organs, he thinks, "have been gradually produced during many generations by the perpetual endeavor of the creatures to supply the want of food, and to have been delivered to their posterity with constant improvement of them for the purposes required."[20]

"The three great objects of desire, which have changed the forms of many animals by their exertions to gratify them are those of lust, hunger, and security."   Animals have acquired weapons to aid them in their combats for "the exclusive possession of the females."   Thus, he points out, "the horny skin on the shoulder of the boar is a defense only against males of his own species."   And the horns of the stag "have been

[19] *Zoonomia*, I, 109.
[20] *Ibid.*, I, 507-8.

formed for the purpose of combating other stags." He all but phrases the law of survival of the fittest when he states, "The final cause of this contest amongst the males seems to be, that the strongest and most active animal should propagate the species, which should thence become improved."[21] The importance of sex life to plants and animals and the superiority of a bisexual process of reproduction to other forms, Darwin stresses with a variety of citation, much of it botanical.

He speculates upon the causes of the colors of birds' eggs, and of hair and feathers. "The colours of many animals seem adapted to their purposes of concealing themselves either to avoid danger, or to spring upon their prey." He instances the colors of snakes, wild cats, and leopards, of birds, moths, and butterflies, which make the creature not easily distinguishable from its background; also the fact that in colder snowy countries many animals become white in winter. These phenomena, he says, "must have some efficient cause; since the uniformity of their production shews it cannot arise from a fortuitous concurrence of circumstances."[22]

Amongst the changes in animals, many, Darwin points out, are produced by artificial cultivation as in domestic animals—horses, dogs, cattle, sheep, rabbits, and pigeons. There is evidence here of the wide departure of these animals from their wild ancestors. All animals, indeed, "undergo perpetual transformations throughout their lifetimes in consequence of their desires and aversions, of their pleasures and their pains, or of irritations, or of associations; and many of these acquired forms or propensities are transmitted to their posterity."[23]

The resemblance of Erasmus Darwin's ideas upon the evolution of life forms to those of the science of today are apparent. But apparent also is the profound difference which makes his explanation antipathetic to the philosophy of the

[21] *Zoonomia*, I, 516. [22] *Ibid.*, I, 516. [23] *Ibid.*, I, 506.

modern scientist. It is not that Darwin believes in the inheritance of acquired characters, for this theory is still a subject of debate, but that he ascribes as the agency of change in plant and animal not the action of external circumstances, the accidents of environment and, therefore, the survival of individuals and species by chance; but attributes the cause of alteration and hence survival to something within the plant or animal. These, seemingly, adapt themselves to the changes in their conditions. On the plane of animal biology the difference of theory is akin to the endless dispute in theology and philosophy between the proponents of free-will and determinism. Darwin, it is evident, believes in free will, even in plants. His conclusions should meet the approbation of M. Bergson. But scientists as a body are reluctant to admit to their problems, already sufficiently difficult, so disturbing a factor. If Erasmus Darwin ever again becomes a great figure in the history of scientific thought it must be only as biological science admits its inability to explain the evolution of life on mechanistic grounds.

In his discussion of heredity and the transmission of acquired characters Darwin advances some very interesting ideas. The living filament which perpetuates life and which is altered by propensities gradually acquired he thinks to be the property of the male. The mother plays a subordinate part, though "as the first nutriment is supplied by the mother, and therefore resembles such nutritive particles, as have been used for her own nutriment or growth, the progeny takes in part the likeness of the mother."[24] The mother's contribution, through nutriment, to the foetus, may cause it to resemble the mother as it advances in life. Disease may thus be hereditary through the mother as through the father. But that the male

[24] *Ibid.*, I, 531.

chiefly molds the character of the offspring Darwin argues with a wealth of botanical analogy.

Inheritance through the male chiefly and with acquired characters "which we can in some measure deliver to our posterity" is at the root of Darwin's natural philosophy. He introduces in this connection a curious modernization of a very ancient belief. "The act of generation cannot exist without being accompanied with ideas," he remarks, and concedes that the phalli worn by Roman matrons "might have effect in producing a greater proportion of male children."[25] But it is to the male that he ascribes the chief power, through the exercise of the imagination, of determining the sex and character of the offspring:

> The potent wish in the productive hour
> Calls to its aid Imagination's power,
> O'er embryon throngs with mystic charm presides,
> And sex from sex the nascent world divides.
> > *Temple of Nature,* II. ll. 117-120.

In the *Zoonomia* Darwin argues at some length this theory of the determination of sex through the imagination of the male parent. "It is not here to be understood, that the first living fibre, which is to form an animal, is produced with any similarity of form to the future animal; but with propensities, or appetences, which shall produce by accretion of parts the similarity of form, feature, or sex, corresponding to the imagination of the father."[26]

The reader will anticipate from the previous sketch of Darwin's ideas a rather roseate picture of the community of plants and animals. If the microscopic ens created by Divine Love is endowed with powers which enable it to evolve in all the life forms culminating in man, the process should be

[25] *Zoonomia,* I, 528.
[26] *Ibid.,* I, 524.

majestic and sublime.   Yet it is in reality, from the human point of view, unspeakably wasteful and cruel.   Darwin is too good a naturalist to ignore his facts, and the struggle for survival which he portrays rivals any of the pictures of a warring world depicted by later evolutionary scientists.

> Yes! smiling Flora drives her armed car
> Through the thick ranks of vegetable war.
> *Temple of Nature,* IV. ll. 41-42.

The ivy strangles the elm, blight and mildew thin the corn, and insects ravage bud and flower.   Beneath the sea the "shark rapacious" devours his prey, the wolf "tears the guiltless lamb," the owl does not spare the nightingale, which, in turn, preys upon the "glowing worm" that "slays the sleeping flower."   Parasites infest the intestines of animals, the Ichneumon deposits its eggs in the backs of caterpillars, the dragonfly is never sated, and the bees, models of civic industry, rob a weaker tribe of its honey "and slay their thousands."

> From Hunger's arm the shafts of Death are hurl'd
> And one great Slaughter-house the warring world!
> *Temple of Nature,* IV. ll. 65-66.

Nor is man exempt.   He, too,

> Ducks to the mandate of resistless fate.

Whereat Darwin describes the state of man in unflattering terms, for man is not only subject to the perils of nature but worsens his state with slavery, luxury, "ebriety," and all their fell consequents.

> . . . and grinning Pain
> With harlot's smiles deluded man salutes,
> Revenging all his cruelties to brutes!
> There the curst spells of Superstition blind,
> And fix her fetters on the tortured mind;
> She bids in dreams tormenting shapes appear,

> With shrieks that shock Imagination's ear,
> E'en o'er the grave a deeper shadow flings,
> And maddening Conscience darts a thousand stings.
> *Temple of Nature,* IV. ll. 80-88.

—lines which forcibly suggest the torments which the Furies bring to Prometheus and Shelley's denunciations of superstition and a religion of vengeance.

Darwin methodically itemizes most of the terrors to which man is victim: avarice, imposture, envy, jealousy; volcanic eruptions, earthquakes, famine, and pestilence. Man is prey both to savage nature and to his own mental defects. Darwin weighs the compensations: the pleasures of nature and of love, of music, of the products of sentiment and taste, of pity, of science, of justice and liberty. And with these man nevertheless is doomed soon to die.

> While births unnumber'd, ere the parents die,
> The hourly waste of lovely life supply.
> *Temple of Nature,* IV. ll. 341-2.

The oak forms ten thousand acorns, the poppy ten thousand seeds. Insects, frogs, fish spawn incredibly and

> —All these, increasing by successive birth,
> Would each o'er people ocean, air, and earth.
> *Temple of Nature,* IV. ll. 367-8.

Then ensues a passage suggestive of Malthus:

> So human progenies, if unrestrain'd
> By climate friended, and by food sustain'd,
> O'er seas and soils, prolific hordes! would spread
> Ere long, and deluge their terraqueous bed;
> But war, and pestilence, disease, and dearth,
> Sweep the superfluous myriads from the earth.
> *Temple of Nature,* IV. ll. 369-374.

To the humanitarian this is a hateful prospect, but to the scientist there are compensations. From the dissolution of living things

> Born to new life unnumber'd insects pant.
> *Temple of Nature,* IV. l. 387.

The round of life is unceasing:

> While Nature sinks in Time's destructive storms,
> The wrecks of Death are but a change of forms.
> *Temple of Nature,* IV. ll. 387-8.

The very substance of earth is but the recrement of extinct forms of life:

> Thus the tall mountains, that emboss the lands,
> Huge isles of rock, and continents of sands,
> Whose dim extent eludes the inquiring sight,
> *Are Mighty Monuments of Past Delight;*
> Shout round the globe, how Reproduction strives
> With vanquish'd Death,—and Happiness survives.
> *Temple of Nature,* IV. ll. 447-452.

It is not, to most, a philosophy which will rouse enthusiasm. Poets have made of it the theme for pessimistic challenges to the Deity. Shelley sought escape from it through Platonic mysticism. Not the mere survival of life sufficed for him, but its humane survival in a world freed from strife and suffering. Yet that Darwin's and kindred scientific pictures of man and his destiny had their increasing effect upon him is evident from a reading of *Queen Mab* and *Prometheus.* In *Queen Mab,* though Shelley borrows Darwin's description of the earth as a "slaughterhouse," the contrast is made essentially between the beauty and harmony of nature and the cruelty and inhumanity of men. There is scant recognition of struggle and cruelty as the law of all life. In *Prometheus* his philosophy recognizes the evil inherent even in the inanimate processes of nature. Not only the animals and man slay each other, but Mother Earth pours forth mephitic vapours and rains down thunder-stones. In the Promethean day, when man throws off his evil nature, all creatures likewise are transformed to good and the natural forces become beneficent.

A scientific stoicism did not suffice for Shelley, but that, in his philosophical evolution, the teachings of science left their deep impress is evident from his acceptance, ultimately, of the slowness of the processes of change. In the eager altruism of his boyhood, mankind was to be soon transformed through the exercise of reason. It was the dream and fallacy of the French radical philosophy of the eighteenth century. In *Prometheus* Shelley clings to his faith in a world ultimately good and beautiful, freed from strife and terror; but its attainment is indefinitely removed. Mercury, messenger of Jupiter, says:

> Yet pause, and plunge
> Into Eternity, where recorded time,
> Even all that we imagine, age on age,
> Seems but a point, and the reluctant mind
> Flags wearily in its unending flight,
> Till it sink, dizzy, blind, lost, shelterless;
> Perchance it has not numbered the slow years
> Which thou must spend in torture, unreprieved?

> *Prometheus.*

> Perchance no thought can count them, yet they pass.
> P. U. I. ll. 416-424.

The attainment of freedom lies in the unfolding nature of *Prometheus* himself. In him, in the growth of his own soul, lies the possibility of release, not in any external aid or pressure of circumstance. And this conception of the force which makes for change and perfectibility harmonizes with the vitalistic theory of Erasmus Darwin. Darwin's evolutionary doctrine is, moreover, reconcilable with the Platonic philosophy to which Shelley more and more inclined as he matured. In Darwin's scheme there is a place for soul. The spirit of animation upon whose resemblances to electricity or some subtler ethereal fluid, Darwin speculates, is scarcely if at all distinguishable from the soul of the universe as conceived by pantheism.

CHAPTER V

HERSCHEL AND COSMIC EVOLUTION

THE PERIOD of the late eighteenth and early nineteenth centuries was marked by great advances in astronomical knowledge, a leading contributor to which was the elder Herschel. His papers, running through many years of the *Philosophical Transactions,* are a record of new discoveries or of the visual verification of astronomical theory. It was as an observational astronomer that he was most notable. Making his own lenses he constructed telescopes surpassing in power any previous instruments. With them he disclosed the magnitude and splendor of the stellar universe as never before guessed. He is thus reported in an interview with Campbell, the poet: "I have looked further into space than ever human being did before me. I have observed stars, of which the light, it can be proved, must take two millions of years to reach this earth."

One of Herschel's chief problems through his long life of observations was to determine the shape and extent of the Milky Way and the place of our solar system therein. To this end he instituted an elaborate system of star counts whereby in a comprehensive survey of the heavens he could determine the number and relative magnitudes of stars in each unit of space. He wished to determine whether the distribution of the stars was uniform, whether the universe had apparent boundaries, and to estimate its probable extent. The reports of his findings cover a period of over thirty years and his ultimate beliefs differ, in one very important respect, from his earlier conclusions.

In his earlier observations "Herschel ventured to lay down the boundaries of the stellar aggregation to which our sun belongs. So far as he 'had yet gone round it,' in 1785, he perceived it to be 'everywhere terminated, and in most places very narrowly too.' "[1] He demonstrated that our sun is a star not far from the bifurcation of the Milky Way. Our solar system, moreover, he discovered to be in motion towards the constellation Hercules. The stars visible to us lie more or less in clusters scattered throughout a comparatively thin, but immensely extended, stratum. The form of this stratum, some of its boundaries, and its probable extent he at first thought he had determined. His ultimate belief, however, was "that when our gages will no longer resolve the milky way into stars, it is not because its nature is ambiguous, but because it is fathomless."[2] The significance of this denial of his former belief, in so far as it relates to Shelley's astronomical allusions, will later appear.

The most intelligible procedure in this survey is to follow the high points of the observations which Herschel conducted in relation to stars and nebulae in his proofs of stellar evolution. His observations and conclusions can be concisely stated and without technical terminology.

The nebular hypothesis was advanced by Kant early in his life when speculating upon natural phenomena. Later it was restated in more mathematical terms by Laplace. Laplace postulates for the solar system an original nebulous mass of which the sun was a central and more condensed mass rotating on its axis. In cooling, the central mass contracted and rotated more rapidly. The outer parts, through the operation of centrifugal force, were left as a ring, which, in turn, cooling and condensing, formed a second sphere and ring. In the succession of these phenomena lay, presumably, the explanation of our solar system of a central sun with attendant planets, some of these accompanied by satellites. The ocular demon-

[1] Agnes M. Clarke, *The Herschels and Modern Astronomy*, 58.
[2] *Collected Scientific Papers of Sir William Herschel*, II. 607.

tration of the general truth of this theory was one of Herschel's chief contributions to astronomy.

The papers covering Herschel's chief "observations relating to the construction of the heavens" appear at intervals in the *Philosophical Transactions* from the year 1811 to the year 1818. He had by the year 1811 given up his earlier belief that the stars of the Milky Way were equally scattered. Also he now distinguished between nebulae and star clusters, which he had formerly confused, and established a series of steps in the evolution of the nebulous stuff, which he took to be the primal substance of the stellar universe, to fully organized systems of suns and planets such as our sun and its satellites. This nebulous stuff occupied the heavens on either side of the Milky Way where the stars became more rare, but was also found in masses within the Milky Way itself and in conjunction with stellar systems but half evolved.

In his paper of 1811[3] Herschel distinguishes carefully between nebulae and star clusters. He then proceeds to classify nebulosities from the primordial extensive diffused nebulosity to nebulous masses of increasing brightness and definiteness of form. As to the principle of condensation apparent in this evolution he remarks:

Instead of inquiring after the nature of the cause of the condensation of nebulous matter, it would indeed be sufficient for the present purpose to call it merely a condensing principle; but since we are already acquainted with the centripetal force of attraction which gives a globular figure to planets, keeps them from flying out of their orbits, and makes one star revolve around another, why should we not look up to the universal gravitation of matter as the cause of every condensation, accumulation, compression, and concentration of the nebulous matter.[4]

The degrees of condensation of nebulae from dimness to brightness, Herschel accounts for by the length of operation,

[3] *Collected Scientific Papers of Sir William Herschel*, II, 459.
[4] *Ibid.*, II, 468.

in each instance, of the attractive principle. In the fall of the
nebulous matter to the nucleus a rotatory movement is evident
which gives motion to the celestial body in its formation. He
traces the development of nebulae as they become condensed,
round, and increasingly bright.

Brightness keeps up with condensation till the increase of it
brings on a consolidation which will no longer permit the internal
penetration of light, and thus a planetary appearance must in the
end be the consequence; for planets are solid opaque bodies, shining only by superficial light, whether it be innate or reflected.[5]

When we reflect upon these circumstances, we may conceive
that, perhaps in progress of time, these nebulae which are already
in such a state of compression, may still be farther condensed so as
actually to become stars.[6]

The total dissimilitude between the appearance of a diffusion
of the nebulous matter and of a star, is so striking, that an idea of
the conversion of the one into the other can hardly occur to any
one who has not before him the result of the critical examination
of the nebulous system which has been displayed in this paper.
The end I have had in view, by arranging my observations in the
order in which they have been placed, has been to show, that the
above mentioned extremes may be connected by such nearly allied
intermediate steps, as will make it highly probable that every succeeding state of the nebulous matter is the result of the action of
gravitation upon it while in a foregoing one, and by such steps
the successive condensation of it has been brought up to the
planetary condition. From this the transit to the stellar form, it
has been shown, requires but a very small additional compression
of the nebulous matter, and several instances have been given
which connect the planetary to the stellar appearance.[7]

In his paper of February 24, 1814,[8] Herschel continued his
study of cosmic evolution from a consideration of nebulae
forming stars and planets to the grouping of the stars. Beginning with a consideration of stars with nebulous matter about

---

[5] *Ibid.*, 486.   [6] *Ibid.*, 487.   [7] *Ibid.*, 495.   [8] *Ibid.*, 520.

them, stars with nebulous branches, nebulous stars, stars connected with extensive windings of nebulosity, small patches of stars mixed with nebulosity, etc., he proceeds to the sidereal part of the heavens. Stars he considers as essentially like our sun and planets.

. . . It follows that stars, although surrounded by a luminous atmosphere, may be looked upon as so many opaque, habitable, planetary globes: differing from what we know of our own planets, only in their size, and by their intrinsically luminous appearance.[9]

Now since the stars of the milky way are permanently exposed to the action of a power whereby they are irresistibly drawn into groups, we may be certain that from mere clustering stars they will be gradually compressed through successive stages of accumulation, more or less resembling the state of some of the 263 objects by which, in the tenth and six succeeding articles, the operation of the clustering power has been laid open to our view, till they come up to what may be called the ripening period of the globular form, and total insulation; from which it is evident that the milky way must be finally broken up, and cease to be a stratum of scattered stars.

We may also draw a very important additional conclusion from the gradual dissolution of the milky way: for the state into which the incessant action of the clustering power has brought it at present, is a kind of chronometer that may be used to measure the time of its past and future existence: and although we do not know the rate of going of this mysterious chronometer, it is nevertheless certain, that since the breaking up of the parts of the milky way affords a proof that it cannot last forever, it equally bears witness that its past duration cannot be admitted to be infinite.[10]

These passages, though brief, suffice to set forth the chief results of Herschel's long and laborious researches. The stellar universe was explicable by the law of gravity known to us on our earth. Newton's *Principia* held true of the Milky Way as

[9] *Collected Scientific Papers of Sir William Herschel*, 529.
[10] *Ibid.*, 540.

a whole as of our tiny solar system. This universe was a finite and evolving one. Though vast it was visibly bordered by nebulous stuff, the primal matter out of which all the integrated systems of suns and planets had evolved. The steps of the process could be observed. Moreover the evolution must continue until the force of gravitation should pull all the matter of the universe to a center and all movement cease. However vast the duration of time necessary to this conclusion it was, clearly, finite.

The stars Herschel considered as essentially like our sun and planets, as "habitable planetary globes," a statement which must have recalled to Shelley the book on science by Adam Walker, who also believed that there were other worlds like ours. A speculation enchanting to the imagination of boyhood was now given weight by the authority of the greatest living astronomer.

Shelley's astronomy is in harmony with Herschel's findings prior to June 11, 1818, upon which date Herschel read a paper seriously altering his conception of the universe, which he had previously supposed to be finite though vast, the stellar stratum of the Milky Way thinning to nebulous stuff at the edges and the whole gravitating to a center and doomed to ultimate extinction. These are Herschel's words:

In these ten observations the gages applied to the milky way were found to be arrested in their progress by the extreme smallness and faintness of the stars; this can however leave no doubt of the progressive extent of the starry regions; for when in one of the observations a faint nebulosity was suspected, the application of a higher magnifying power evinced, that the doubtful appearance was owing to an intermixture of many stars that were too minute to be distinctly perceived with the lower power; hence we may conclude, that when our gages will no longer resolve the milky way into stars, it is not because its nature is ambiguous, but because it is fathomless.[11]

[11] *Ibid.*, II, 609.

This admission alters wholly Herschel's early conception. The stellar universe might, so far as he could tell, be infinite in extent. And if so it must likewise be infinite in its duration and its extinction through the force of gravitation no longer predictable. Shelley, however, it is evident, was unaware of Herschel's newer view, for on March 12, 1818, three months before Herschel's paper was read, Shelley had left for Italy. It is clear from Shelley's astronomy as set forth in *Prometheus* that he is exploiting a theory which Herschel no longer held. It was, of course, highly unlikely that in the Italy of 1818 Shelley should soon have read of Herschel's latest announcement. All intelligence moved slowly at that date, Shelley was inadequately and tardily supplied with books and periodicals, and there is no reason to suppose that he was up to the minute in astronomy or any other science.

There is, to be sure, no evidence that Shelley read Herschel in those papers reported in the proceedings of the Royal Society. What is more probable is that he read some such scientific monthly as the excellent *Nicholson's Journal,* which reported the latest scientific discoveries, gave readable summaries of important papers, and enabled one interested in science, though not a specialist therein, to acquire a sound reading knowledge of scientific theory and advances. The particular source of Shelley's knowledge of science is not in most instances of much moment. If in some one or several of the scientific investigators and theorists of the time can be found data which make Shelley's scientific conceptions as set forth in *Prometheus* fully intelligible, that fact suffices for purposes of interpretation. Scientists mentioned in Shelley's letters, and the scientific encyclopedias of Nicholson and Rees, mentioned in Shelley's notes to *Queen Mab,* are of course, on the face of it, primary sources of his knowledge. Shelley's astronomical lore harmonizes with the findings and theories of Herschel as reported prior to 1818. Herschel may, therefore, be used to interpret Shelley.

The applicability of this method in deciphering Shelley is evident in the two other scientific discoveries of Herschel which are pertinent to our inquiry, that of the infra-red rays of the spectrum, and of active volcanoes on the moon. In a paper read in 1800 Herschel reported the discovery of heat rays below the lowest visible rays of the spectrum. The experiment had been instituted in order to throw more light upon the degree of heat which accompanied various colors as refracted by the spectrum. In making his tests Herschel discovered that the heat increased towards the lower end of the spectrum, that red rays were accompanied by the most heat, and, further, that beyond the point of visibility there were rays which produced heat. This is one of Herschel's statements:

The first four experiments prove, that the maximum of the heating power is vested among the invisible rays; and is probably not less than half an inch beyond the last visible ones. . . . The same experiments also shew, that the sun's visible rays, in their less refrangible state, and considerably beyond the maximum, still exert a heating power fully equal to that of red-coloured light; and that consequently, if we may infer the quantity of the efficient from the effects produced, the invisible rays of the sun probably far exceed the visible ones in number.[12]

Herschel believed it to be "established by incontrovertible facts, that there are rays of heat, both solar and terrestrial, not endowed with the power of rendering objects visible."[13] He concludes that heat and light rays, though found together in solar light, are different, and that heat is less refrangible than light. "The law by which heat is transmitted, is different from that which directs the passage of light; and in that case it must become an irrefragable argument of the difference of the rays which occasion them."[14]

[12] *Collected Scientific Papers of Sir William Herschel*, I, 53 *et seq.*
[13] *Ibid.*, II, 128.   [14] *Ibid.*, II, 137.

This was a great discovery, one which excited widespread interest. Coleridge in a letter to Humphry Davy inquires the chemist's opinion with regard to it. Some of the physicists violently disputed Herschel's findings, believing, apparently, that he had trespassed upon a field of inquiry not proper to an astronomer, and endeavoring to refute him. But later experimentation demonstrated that Herschel's methods were sound and his findings authentic. Shelley's allusions to the dark rays will be evident in several passages later to be cited from the *Prometheus*. Clearly it is an idea to stimulate the philosophic mind bent upon unifying scientific explanations of matter and energy and harmonizing them with metaphysics.

Herschel's dark rays are linked in Shelley's allusions in *Prometheus Unbound,* as I shall later show, with the supposed discovery of active volcanoes on the moon. These important, and in the light of modern science, inexplicable observations, are cited in Erasmus Darwin's notes. The supposed discovery is set forth in Herschel's paper read before the Philosophical Society entitled "An Account of Three Volcanoes in the Moon."[15] In it he discusses volcanoes in the moon which he has seen in process of eruption. The statement is explicit and Herschel expresses no doubt whatsoever as to the nature of the phenomenon. Therein lies, in part, Shelley's justification for his picture in *Prometheus* of the reanimation of the moon, when, in the Promethean age, its frozen veins are thawed.

[15] *Collected Scientific Papers of Sir William Herschel,* I, 315 *et seq.*

CHAPTER VI

NEWTON AND A METAPHYSICAL CONCEPTION OF MATTER

HERSCHEL in his observations in proof of the nebular hypothesis found the law of gravitation as demonstrated by Newton adequate to explain the phenomena of cosmic evolution. Newton's great work lies as a foundation stone to later science. Its simplicity and comprehensiveness revolutionized astronomy and physics; and the *Principia* stands for scientists in other fields as an ideal at which to aim. It is impossible to exaggerate its importance as the magnetic core of later science, around which subsidiary discoveries arranged themselves in patterns which seemed to promise ultimately a unified, related, and intelligible design interpretative of all scientific knowledge.

For the purposes of this study three aspects of Newton's demonstration and theory are briefly to be considered: (1) his work in optics, the influence of which in Shelley is evident in certain passages upon light and color; (2) his hypothesis of the luminiferous ether, which, designed to explain the phenomena of light and gravitation, is, in Newton's speculations, made to serve also as a partial explanation of electricity, magnetism, the constitution of matter, and the spirit of animation; (3) the metaphysical implications of Newton's theory of the ether. Newton himself left the domain of natural science and carried his speculations into theology and philosophy. His ultimate theory is mystical. And in this derivative of his scientific work he has as greatly influenced philosophers and theologians as in his mathematical astronomy and physics he has influenced scientists.

Shelley's interest in light and color is everywhere manifest in his verse. Vision was to him the master sense. He is essentially an eye-minded poet. Sound, touch, and smell are vastly less important in his sensational experience. And being also a man of scientific interests it is natural enough that he should seek explanations of the phenomena of light to which, as a poet, he was acutely sensitive. In Newton's *Opticks,* or in the scientific writing subsequent which is based on Newton, lie explanations which serve to elucidate some of Shelley's lines. That Shelley read the *Opticks* is not certain, though two allusions to Newton may be noted in his letters. But the copious work upon the phenomena of light to be found in Shelley's day suffices to explain his knowledge.[1]

Variety of colors, says Newton, "depends upon the composition of light." For, "If the sun's light consisted of but one sort of rays there would be but one color in the whole world."[2] He points out that it would be impossible to produce any other by whatever process of reflexion and refraction. The sun's light "is mixed of several sorts of rays . . . and . . . keep those their original properties perpetually the same without alteration."[3] All the various colors of the world arise, then, "from the original colorific qualities of the rays whereof the lights consist by which those colors are seen."[4]

Colors in objects are due to the fact that bodies each reflect more of certain kinds of rays than of others. Minium, because it reflects the least frangible or red-making rays most copiously, appears to be red. "Violets reflect the most refrangible, most copiously, and thence have their colour, and so of other bodies. Every body reflects the rays of its own color more copiously than the rest."[5] The appearances of colours "are

---

[1] An instance, an article in *Nicholson's Journal* for June 1802 by Professor Thomas Young of the Royal Institution. Professor Young collects various passages from Newton's writings that relate to the luminiferous ether.

[2] Newton, *Opticks,* I, 2, p. 90 (1704).

[3] *Ibid.,* p. 119.

[4] *Ibid.,* p. 119.

[5] *Ibid.,* p. 135.

derived not from any physical change caused in light by refraction or reflection, but only from the various mixtures or separations of rays, by virtue of their different refrangibility or reflexibility."[6]

The rainbow is "made by refraction of the sun's light in drops of falling rain."[7]   The halo about sun and moon is due to the prismatic action of light on hail-stones.[8]   Sea water absorbs red and reflects violet and blue most easily.[9]   There is some relation of colours to the lengths of musical chords.[10] When globules of rain "become of a convenient size to reflect some colours and transmit others [they] may constitute clouds of various colours according to their sizes."[11] Air also serves to refract light.[12]   If bodies are to look black "it is necessary that many rays be stopt, retained, and lost in them,"[13] and it follows that "black substances do soonest of all others become hot in the sun's light and burn."[14]

Colors, then, reside not in objects themselves but in the power of these objects to absorb and reflect the various constituent colored rays which compose the white light of the sun. The vibration length of these rays varies, the shortest vibration, acting upon the optic nerve, giving the sensation of red; and other colors in the same way being determined by the length of the light vibrations.[15]   Harmony and discord in color, may, Newton thinks, "arise from the proportions of the vibrations propagated through the fibres of the optic nerves into the brain."[16]   He draws an analogy from the harmony and disharmony of sounds.   Strictly, then, color is a sensation in the brain dependent upon the length of the light waves which beat upon the optic nerve.

The ether, in Newton's hypothesis, provides a medium for

[6] *Ibid.*, II, 2, p. 48.   [10] *Ibid.*, II, 1, p. 18.   [14] *Ibid.*, p. 63.
[7] *Ibid.*, I, 2, p. 126.   [11] *Ibid.*, II, 1, p. 57.   [15] *Ibid.*, Query 13.
[8] *Ibid.*, p. 134.   [12] *Ibid.*, II, 2, p. 73-4.   [16] *Ibid.*, Query 14.
[9] *Ibid.*, p. 139.   [13] *Ibid., p. 169.*

the action of gravitation, and one susceptible also to vibrations. In a letter to Oldenburg, Newton explains his theory of the ether in contradistinction to Hooke's theory based on Des Cartes. "In all this I have nothing in common with him, but the supposition that ether is a medium susceptible of vibrations, of which supposition I make a very different use; he supposing it light itself, which I suppose it is not."[17] Heat and light he conceived as conveyed through a vacuum by the vibrations of this ether, "a much subtler medium than air."[18] This he conceived to pervade all bodies and to be expanded through the heavens, its resistance so small as to be inconsiderable. He supposes it to be more elastic than our air "and above 700,000 times more rare."[19] Of the nature of light he will commit himself no farther than to say that "it is something or other capable of exciting vibrations in the ether."[20]

Ether, an elastic medium capable of vibrations and the transmission of light and heat, the means, also, for the exercise through space of that attractive force known as the force of gravitation, is in Newton's conception not homogeneous in substance. It consists "of the main phlegmatic body of air intermixed with various vapours and exhalations. For the electric and magnetic effluvia and the gravitating principle seem to argue such variety."[21] "Electric effluvia," at least, "warrant the assumption of such ethereal spirits."[22] Mr. A. J. Snow, in his examination of Newton's theories, thinks that Newton was familiar with the work of Gilbert and Boyle and in ascribing certain electric and magnetic powers to the ether is indebted to them. Inasmuch as electrical and magnetic

[17] Newton, Letter to Oldenburg, Dec. 21, 1675.
[18] *Opticks,* Query 18, 22.
[19] *Ibid.*
[20] Birch, *History of the Royal Society,* III, 249.
[21] Cited by A. J. Snow, in *Matter and Gravity in Newton's Physical Philosophy,* 140.
[22] *Ibid.*

theory are especially germane to our inquiry into Shelley's scientific background, some summary of Mr. Snow's discussion is timely.

William Gilbert, the first observer of genuine scientific importance in the field of electricity and magnetism, in his speculations endeavors to identify attractive forces with the peculiar "effluvia" of electricity and magnetism. "It is very probable that a magnetic or electric such as we find in amber exhales something peculiar that attracts the bodies themselves, and not the air. . . .[23] A breath, then, proceeding from a body that is a concretion of moisture or aqueous fluid, reaches the body that is to be attracted, and as soon as it is reached it is united to the attracting electric." Two bodies thus in touch become one, are in "most intimate harmony, and that is what is meant by attraction."[24] Mr. Snow points out the close similarity of this idea to Newton's. The ethereal spirits or the "effluvia" of Newton are "when applied to magnetic or electrical forces . . . the principle which directly, by means of contact, draws together or asunder particles of matter."[25] And Mr. Snow further remarks: "We must always keep in mind that Newton put in the same category all attracting forces, whether their function be gravity, magnetism, or electricity."[26]

Gilbert's association of electrical attraction with moisture is shrewd. He declared, also, that the earth is a great loadstone exhibiting characteristic powers of attraction. He thought the interior of the earth to be "composed of a homogeneous magnetic mass."[27] All bodies he conceived to be magnetic or potentially so. The moon, like the earth, is magnetic and the influence which they exert one on the other is reciprocal.

[23] Gilbert, *Loadstone and Magnetic Bodies,* 89. Cited by Snow, p. 180.
[24] *Ibid.,* 91. Cited by Snow, p. 180.
[25] Snow, 180.
[26] *Ibid.,* 176.
[27] *Ibid.,* 176.

The force which emanates from the moon reaches to the earth, and, in like manner, the magnetic virtue of the earth pervades the region of the moon: both correspond and conspire by the joint action of both, according to a proportion and conformity of motions, but the earth has more effect in consequence of its superior mass; the earth attracts and repels the moon, and the moon within certain limits, the earth; not so as to make the bodies come together, as magnetic bodies do, but so that they may go on in a continuous course.[28]

Gilbert develops two general axioms or rules: "The matter of the earth's globe is brought together and held together by itself electrically; (2) that the earth's globe is directed and revolves magnetically."[29]   Electricity and magnetism are, evidently, employed to characterize two manifestations of the one force, a force similar to if not identifiable with the "attraction" whose operation Newton made the thesis of his mathematical demonstrations and for whose functioning he postulated the ether.

In Gilbert's theory, earth and moon are loadstones mutually attractive; electricity and magnetism are names for two operations of the same force; and for each of the planetary bodies he imagines a "soul" which, residing within, projects its power, its "effused immaterial forms" within the limits of its own sphere or range of influence.[30]   Planets must keep to their orbits and not trespass upon the domains of others.   The word "soul" in this connection is highly interesting, for whether used in a spiritual or merely figurative way its suggestion of animation, of mind, gives currency to later employment of the word in a mystical sense.   John Wesley, in the middle of

[28] Gilbert, *De Mundo Nostro Sublunari Philosophia nova* (1631), 186. Cited by Snow.
[29] Gilbert, *Loadstone and Magnetic Bodies,* 97.   Cited by Snow, 177.
[30] Snow, 182.

the eighteenth century, remarked that electricity was the "soul of the universe."[31]

In the speculations of Harvey, discoverer of the circulation of the blood, the spirit of animation, "the heat of animals which is not fire and does not take its origin from fire," derives from the "solar ray." In a rhapsodic passage Harvey thus describes the function of the blood and its mystical and animating powers:

The blood, when present within the veins as part of a body, a generative part, too, and endowed with soul, being the soul's immediate instrument, and primary seat . . . the blood, seeming also to have a share of another diviner body and being diffused with divine heat, suddenly acquires extraordinary powers, and is analogous to the elements of the stars. As spirits, the blood is the hearth, the vesta, the household deity, the innate heat, the sun of the microcosm, the fire of Plato; not because it shines, burns, and destroys like common fire, but because it preserves, and nourishes, and increases its very self by its perpetual wandering motion . . . constructs and adjoins to itself, even as the heavenly bodies above, especially the sun and moon, impart life to what is below, while they continue in perpetual circulation. Since, therefore, the blood acts beyond the powers of the elements, and is potent with those virtues aforesaid, and also is the instrument of the supreme workman, no one will give praise enough to its wonderful and divine faculties.[32]

In Gilbert and Harvey lie, then, antecedents of Newton's ascription to his hypothetical ether of these various forces: attraction, electricity, magnetism, and the spirit of animation. In Newton's contemporary, Boyle, early discoverer of the laws of gases, the surmises of these preceding scientists are reaffirmed, and the character of the "ether" is more narrowly

[31] *Bibliographical History of Electricity and Magnetism,* Paul Fleury Mottelay (1922).

[32] "On Generation," in *The Works of William Harvey,* translated by R. Willis, London, 1847, LXXI, 510, 1. 15-40. Cited by Snow, 171.

defined. "In the ether of the ancients," Boyle writes, "there was nothing taken notice of but a diffused and very subtle substance, yet we are at present content to allow that there is always in the air a swarm of streams moving in a determined course betwixt the north pole and the south; which substance we should not probably have dreamed of, if our inquisitive Gilbert had not happily found out the magnetism of the terrestrial globe."[33]

The analogy of the spirit of animation to the nature of light is made by Boyle explicitly. The passage is somewhat long as summing up much precedent theory and making clear Newton's ascription to the ether of so great and so mysterious powers.

Not only the air, by reason of its thinness and subtility, is capable of being thus penetrated, moved, and altered, by these planetary virtues and lights; but forasmuch also as our *spirits,* and the *spirits likewise* of all mixed bodies, are really of an *aerious, ethereal, luminous production,* and *composition;* these spirits therefore of ours, and the spirits of all other bodies, must necessarily no less suffer an impression from the same lights, and cannot be less subject to an alteration, motion, agitation, and infection through them and by them, than the other, viz. the air: but rather as our *spirits* are more near and more analogous to the nature of light than the air, so they must be more prone and easy to be impressed than it. And if our *spirits,* and the *spirits* of all mixed bodies, may be altered, changed, moved and impressed by these superior bodies, and their properties; then these spirits being the only principles of energy, power, force, and life, in all bodies wherein they are, and the immediate causes through which all alteration comes to the bodies themselves; it is impossible therefore spirits should be altered and changed, and yet no alteration made in the bodies themselves: and therefore a less limit or extreme cannot be set to the power or operation, or force of the superior bodies upon the inferior, than what must terminate at length into the very bodies

[33] Boyle, *Cosmical Suspicions, Appendix to the Cosmical Qualities of Things,* III, 316-17. Cited by Snow, 175.

themselves . . . as the sun shining on the rest of the planets doth not . . . only barely illuminate their bodies; but besides this . . . [a body] . . . is not only enlightened, warmed, cherished and fructified, by the power, virtue, and influence of the sun, but hath its proper magnetical planetary virtue also fermented, stirred, agitated and awakened in it, which it remits back with the reflected light of the sun. . . .[34]

To return, now, to Newton's theory of the ether, the elastic and rare medium through which are executed the forces of gravitation, electricity, and magnetism. In a notable letter to Oldenburg having to do with the revision of a scientific paper he ascribes to the ether the origin of matter itself.

When I say that the frame of nature may be nothing but ether condensed by a fermental principle, instead of those words write that it may be nothing but various contextures of some certain ethereal spirits, or vapours, condensed as it were by precipitation, much after the manner that vapours are condensed into water, or exhalations into grosser subtances, though not so easily condensible; and after condensation wrought into various forms, at first by the immediate hand of the creator, and ever since by the power of nature. . . . Thus perhaps may all things be originated from ether.

A little after, where I say the ethereal spirit may be condensed in fermenting or burning bodies, or otherwise inspissated in the pores of the earth to a tender matter, which may be as it were, the succus nutritius of the earth, or primary substances, out of which things generable grow; instead of this, you may write, that that spirit may be condensed in fermenting or burning bodies, or otherwise coagulated in the pores of the earth and water, into some kind of humid active matter for the continual uses of nature, adhering to the sides of those pores after the manner that vapours condense on the sides of a vessel.[35]

It is at, or about, this point in Newton's theory of the ether that the reader of Newton is uncertain whether the dis-

[34] Cited by Snow, 187.
[35] Newton, Letter to Oldenburg, Jan. 25, 1675-6.

cussion remains still in the realm of physical theory or has become metaphysical. In the ensuing passage the line of demarcation seems to be evident. After discussing the character of the ethereal medium composed "of the main phlegmatic body of air intermixed with various vapors and exhalations," Newton goes on to say, "so may the gravitating attraction of the earth be caused by the continual condensation of some other such like ethereal spirit; not of the main body of phlegmatic ether, but of something very thinly and subtly diffused through it, perhaps of an unctuous, or gummy tenacious, and springy nature; and bearing much the same relations to ether which the vital aerial spirit requisite for the conservation of flame and vital motions does to air."[36] And after describing the circulation and metamorphoses of this "ethereal spirit" he surmises: "And as the earth, so perhaps may the sun imbibe this spirit copiously, to conserve his shining, and keep the planets from receding further from him: and they that will may also suppose that this spirit affords or carries with it thither the solary fuel and material principle of light, and that the vast ethereal spaces between us and the stars are for a sufficient repository for this food of the sun and planets."[37]

In the last paragraph of all the editions of the *Principia* Newton advanced the same theory or question, speaking of "a certain most subtle Spirit" through which the force of gravitation and the action of electricity are made manifest; whereby, also, "All sensation is excited, and the members of animal bodies move at the command of the will, namely, by the vibrations of this Spirit, mutually propagated along the solid filaments of the nerves." We have not, he concludes, "sufficiency of experiments" to demonstrate "the laws by which this electric and elastic Spirit operates."

[36] Cited by Snow, 140-142, from Newton's paper of Dec. 9, 1675, sent to the Royal Society.

[37] *Ibid.*

Mr. Snow, in his discussion of the problems raised by Newton's variations in phraseology when characterizing the ether, puts the question thus: "Did or did not Newton really conceive the 'subtle spirit'—an *immaterial* and *non-mechanical* entity—to be the same as the mechanically described ether?"[38] For the purposes of astronomy and mathematics Newton's hypotheses were conservative, such as were capable of mathematical expression. As a scientist he was, Mr. Snow deems, cautious. But his speculations went beyond the realm of the physical. Gravitation, though capable of mathematical statement was, Newton conceived, ultimately due to a metaphysical cause inasmuch as bodies act upon each other at a distance through an immaterial medium.

In passing beyond the realm of physics into that of metaphysics Newton links up with the thought of the neo-Platonists, his predecessors and contemporaries. Gilbert had spoken of attractive forces as being "spiritual" and "non-corporeal," not meaning thereby something spiritual or divine "but rather something extremely thin, *e.g.* a breath, very thin air, or vapour."[39] But in Henry More this tenuous physical substance has become spiritual substance and is "attributed by More to God, the Angels, the mind of man, and to space."[40] According to More the functions of this "immaterial cause" are various: "It is the source of motion, of cohesion, or separation of parts of bodies, it is the directing force of all motion, and the source of animal and human locomotion."[41] Back of the manifestations of force and matter, lies, in More's Platonic theory, a Spirit of Nature, an "all-comprehensive and eternal Counsel for the ordering and the guiding of the Motion of Matter."[42]

---

[38] Snow, 166 *et seq.*
[39] *Ibid.*, 182.
[40] *Ibid.*, 198.
[41] *Ibid.*, 197.
[42] Cited by Snow, 195.

Newton's ultimate belief, then, transcending the restrictions of science, is a mystical one, with resemblance to the doctrines of neo-Platonism. God's presence is everywhere. He is the "Soul of the World." The soul of God is space, "but as 'God needs no particular organ to operate' as the human soul does, God and His divine sensorium are the same."[43] Though matter follows the laws of mechanics "the real or final Cause of motion does not, but a Divine Providence creates, conserves, and regulates motion, in order that 'bodies may not go off their course.'"[44]

Stripped of its theological terminology so offensive to the scientific ear, Newton's ultimate philosophy reduces itself to some such belief as this: Permeating the universe, and self-renewed without loss, is energy infinitely tenuous and diffused, the primal something out of which the whole of the cosmos comes into being. This infinite energy is manifested variously in the activities or forces of light, heat, attraction, magnetism, electricity, and animation. The ether, the name by which the mysterious energy is called, either is transformed into these various forces or these forces are functions of its being, the latter seeming to be the case insofar as one may interpret Newton's theory of the ether in its relation to light. And not only is the ether energy, it is also the source of matter. Newton seems to regard matter as, so to speak, the sediment of energy, energy at the lowest stage of its cycle of transformations. Matter, moreover, though seeming solid is, in reality, exceedingly tenuous, permeated to the core by the subtle ether and, seemingly, reconvertible into it.

In some of his characterizations of it Newton calls the ether "electric," but whether with the idea of identifying ether and electricity is not clear. In view of the scanty knowledge of electricity in Newton's day it seems improbable

<hr>

[43] Snow, 209.   [44] *Ibid.*, 209.

that he would postulate such an identity. The powers of electricity, however vast, might not suffice to satisfy all the demands which, in Newton's scheme, are laid upon the supposititious ether. Yet with the growing discoveries made during the eighteenth century in the realm of electricity, and its identification with lightning, it is easy to see whence John Wesley could derive his figure of electricity as the "soul of the universe." If ether constitutes the soul and being of God and the ether is, as may be, but electricity, then electricity is quite literally the "soul of the universe."

If, in Newton's philosophy, motion is conceived of as the attribute of mind in contradistinction with the lifelessness and inertness of matter, the implications of his theory resolve this dualism into a monism. For matter itself, in Newton's hypothesis, is but a lower form of energy, energy relatively quiescent and capable of reconversion into its original form. The whole of the universe is but energy in various manifestations, and the sum of this energy is God. The idea would seem inevitably pantheistic and therein disconcerting to an orthodox believer, as evidently it was to Newton. Though precisely why a pantheistic philosophy is incompatible with Christian belief, unless the latter is unduly doctrinal, I cannot conceive. At any rate, those to whom theological hair-splitting is of no moment can find in Newton basis for a pantheism which unifies contradictory philosophies as well, perhaps, as any other, a belief moreover sanctioned by the name of one of the greatest of scientific thinkers. Science and mysticism touch hands.

There are neo-Platonic notes in this philosophy of Newton's. Matter, to Plotinus, is on the verge of reality, the something most remote from the central source of all life, the mind of God. So, too, in Newton's conception, matter is apparently the lowest manifestation of the divine energy,

energy in its most inert phase, and therefore farthest removed from mind, if mind is identifiable with motion or, perhaps more accurately, with the power to give motion. Both philosophies clearly are immaterial in their emphasis, and troublesome "matter" is made to take a subservient place.

That Newton proceeded farther along the Platonic path to wrestle with the nature of the divine mind itself, and the place of "ideas" or patterns and their realization in a world of animate creation, does not appear. He seems to have found sufficient difficulty in reconciling the implications of his scientific thought with a restricted seventeenth century Biblical theology. But that the sub-current of Platonism which underlies the rationalism of the eighteenth century found comfort and solace in Newton must, I think, be evident. Platonism flourishes not only in the speculations of Berkeley but in poetry and fiction. The Romantic Movement, in the works of Blake, Keats, Wordsworth, and Shelley, is markedly Platonistic, if by the word, so loosely and vaguely used, we mean mystical; mystical in a sense analogous to the mysticism of Platonism and neo-Platonism, however, in particular authors, obscurely and variously derived.

This book does not trespass upon Platonism. It is concerned with the sources of Shelley's scientific ideas and the expression of those ideas in his poetry. That scientific thought very quickly verges upon mysticism in his verse is quite true. His effort in *Prometheus* is precisely to reconcile science and metaphysics, a materialistic and a mystical philosophy. The growth of his mind was away from scepticism and determinism as expressed in typical eighteenth century thought— Hume, Holbach, and the rest—to a belief which, if more difficult to formulate and express, gave him nevertheless more spiritual satisfaction. Berkeley is a step away from Hume to Plato. But Shelley, being interested in science no less than in philosophy, must needs incorporate his scientific thought in any synthesis he might achieve. And to this end the speculations of Newton, whether derived by Shelley at first or second hand, point the way. In Newton, and with the weight and sanction of a great name, the "material" phenomena of the physical universe derive from an "immaterial" source.

CHAPTER VII

HUMPHRY DAVY AND AN ELECTRICAL THEORY OF MATTER

Humphry Davy, like Erasmus Darwin, Herschel, and Newton, was a scientist with imagination. He wrote considerable poetry, some of which is not unlike Wordsworth's poorer verse. Man of the world, popular, successful, jealous of gifted subordinates, it is difficult for one not versed in science to assess his worth as an investigator. Yet he is indisputably the discoverer of several new elements and one of the successful adapters, if not the sole discoverer, of the electro-analytic method in chemical research. A speculative mind, surely, one fertile in suggestion for a poet, such as Shelley, with a scientific bent. In Davy, Newton's theories reappear, but modified by the progress made in chemistry and electricity in the hundred and twenty-five years that lie between them. In Davy's speculations ideas traceable to Newton assume a dress that is remarkably modern, some of them all but anticipating the form which they assume in contemporary science.

Modern chemistry, the chemistry of Dalton, Priestley, and Lavoisier, was so completely in its infancy when Davy, as a very young man, became interested in it, that with a few months of application he was enabled to make genuine discoveries. Engaged as the chemical expert for a "pneumatic institution" at Bristol, a sanitarium which employed various gases in the treatment of disease, he made exhaustive researches into the character of nitrous oxide, the gas which Priestley had discovered; was engaged by the Royal Society, became a popular lecturer and demonstrator on scientific subjects, and soon thereafter announced various discoveries of importance. Contemporary scientists, though forced to acknowledge his

contributions, apparently distrusted his penchant for speculation. It was a weakness of which he was himself aware, and
his later scientific pronouncements are more cautious than his
earlier ones. His brother, in his memoirs, gives apologetically
only parts of some of these; unfortunately so, for they have,
if still in existence, proved inaccessible to me and may have
made precisely the imaginative statements of scientific theory
which most attracted Shelley. There is, however, in what is
extant and accessible of Davy, sufficient to explain certain scientific speculations employed by Shelley in *Prometheus,* and
the general tenor of Davy's theory is, I believe, evident.

In his work upon nitrous oxide Davy was able to produce
the gas in a pure form and to demonstrate its kinship with
other gases associated with its manufacture. I shall cite those
aspects of his discoveries that seem to have bearing upon Shelley's knowledge of this group of gases as, and if, alluded to
in *Prometheus.* After applying heat to a small quantity of
nitrous acid Davy observes that "the colour of the fluid gradually changed to a deep red . . . and in a short time deep
red vapour began to fill the tube."[1] This when condensed
"resolved itself into nitrous gas." The color was apparently
due to contact with air: "On mingling a little of it with
atmospheric air, it gave a red vapour, and diminished. . . .
it was nitrous gas nearly pure."[2] If the allusion in *Prometheus*
is to this gas, the epithet "crimson" which Shelley employs
is the key to its identity.

The association of nitrous gas, and nitrous oxide, with
carbonic acid gas is evident from another citation having to
do with the decomposition of nitre by charcoal. "The products instead of being simply carbonic acid and nitrogen, are
carbonic acid, nitrogen, nitrous acid, probably ammonia, and

[1] Davy, *Collected Works,* III, 17.
[2] *Ibid.,* 99.

sometimes nitrous gas."[3]   And his experiments show the close
association of carbonic acid with nitrous oxide in the production of the latter—the association of a mephitic gas with one
which had qualities most beneficent to the life of animals
and plants or was so thought to have at that time. "During
the solution of vegetable matters in nitric acid, by heat, very
minute portions of nitrous oxide are sometimes produced,
always, however, mingled with large quantities of nitrous
gas, and carbonic acid."[4]   Yet, Davy remarks, "there are no
reasons for supposing that nitrous oxide is formed in any of
the processes of nature."[5]

But why these dry and technical details with regard to the
composition of gases whose properties and even whose nomenclature are confusing to the non-scientific reader? It is
difficult for us to recapture that passion for "airs," as they
were first called, which consumed scientists and health seekers
in the year 1800. A whole new series of gases was coming
into being whose properties were unknown but which, it
was thought, might effect miracles. Especially gases were
looked to as curative agents, and "pneumatic institutions,"
such as that with which Humphry Davy was early associated,
flourished for a time. It was a fad which soon declined, for
the beneficent results were negligible. More significant to the
minds of scientist and philosopher was the part played by
gases in the life histories of plants and animals and in the
endless round of atmospheric change. Erasmus Darwin's
interest in this theme has been demonstrated. Davy, likewise, was fond of impressing audiences at his popular lectures
with pictures of the complex economy of nature's laboratory.
Shelley's scientific interests would be suspect did not gases
play a considerable part in them.

Davy in his experiments subjected various plants to nitrous

[3] Davy, *Collected Works*, 32.   [4] *Ibid.*, 132.   [5] *Ibid.*, 138.

oxide and several other gases in the effort to determine which gases were absorbed and with what effects. It was known that nitrogen, so largely a constituent of plant life, was absorbed from the air, water, and soil, but the precise chemistry involved was unknown. It is not apparent that Davy's experiments were, in this respect, particularly instructive. A rose kept in nitrous oxide "speedily faded and died." Davy had thought "its colors might be rendered brighter by gas." Six mint plants were put in phials containing six gases. That in carbonic acid faded in two days and in four was dead; that in hydrogen died in less than five days; that in nitrous oxide faded little for the first two days, but drooped in the third and was dead in the same time as that in hydrogen; in oxygen, flourished with a finer green for four days, but in ten days lost all its leaves; in common air was sickly and yellow at the end of ten days; in hydrocarbonate was greener and more flourishing than ever.

Davy's most notable contribution to the study of gases and that most widely advertised had to do with nitrous oxide, or laughing gas, and its effects when inhaled. Davy was intrepid in experimenting upon himself and with nitrous oxide determined thereby its anesthetic and inebriating effects. Of the former he concluded: "As nitrous oxide in its extensive operation appears capable of destroying physical pain, it may probably be used with advantage during surgical operations in which no great effusion of blood takes place."[6] Philosophically more interesting is an anticipation of the psychological effects noted at a much later date in the ether trance. Davy, having inhaled nitrous oxide, was exhilarated and exclaimed to his assistant: "Nothing exists but thoughts! the universe is composed of impressions, ideas, pleasures, and pains."[7]

[6] *Ibid.*, 329.
[7] *Memoirs of the Life of Sir Humphry Davy*, I, 99.

Shelley would have coveted so complete an anticipation of the Platonic heaven. That he himself experimented with the effects of the gas is not known. But it would be surprising had he not. A large number of Davy's contemporaries including among poets, Coleridge and Southey, are on record as having done so; with various effects, to be sure, and few with such mystical elation as Davy experienced.

Davy in his public lectures aimed to entertain and instruct; to give to his auditors a somewhat rounded picture of the natural universe. Various sciences other than chemistry enter into his explanations of things: especially meteorology, electricity, and to some degree, geology. In the latter, he sets forth the theory of Leibnitz and Whiston which Shelley, in *Prometheus,* renders in verse, that a catastrophic deluge was, at an early period of the earth's history, caused by the attraction of a large comet. An exact citation of this view will later be made when Shelley's lines are annotated.

The renovating principle in nature Davy describes both in its animate and inanimate aspects. Vegetation destroys the carbonic acid gas in the air and liberates oxygen necessary to the life of animals. Beneath these processes, in the earth itself, the round of renovation and decay pursues a similar cycle. "The influence of air and water upon our existing land is continually tending to degrade and decompose it; and our rivers are constantly carrying the divided matter of soils into the sea."[8] The renovating principle Davy depicts as the action of water and air upon the metals of the earth exposed as the surface is worn away. Further, electricity plays its part: "In the general economy of nature, electrical currents, probably the same as those exhibited in the Aurora Borealis and Australis, may be the means of disuniting inflammable matters from oxygen, and separating

[8] From a lecture of 1811. *Memoirs,* I, 398.

metals from their combinations, so as to preserve a constant and uniform relation between the solid, the fluid, and the aeriform parts of the globe."[9]

"Alterations of electrical equilibrium are continually taking place in nature."[10] Some of these are violent, such as accompany earthquakes and volcanic eruptions.   Others are "constant and tranquil" in the interior strata of the globe. "Electricity must be continually manifested" where certain metals come in contact, and other chemical combinations such as occur in nature must likewise generate electricity which is instrumental in the electro-chemical cycle of decay and regeneration. It is not in its spectacular activities that it is most potent. "Generally diffused, like heat it, perhaps, is equally active, equally important, in the economy of nature."[11]

In his first Bakerian lecture, in 1806, entitled "On Some Chemical Agencies of Electricity," Davy developed the electrochemical theory to which he afterwards adhered. Later a controversy ensued as to priority in certain applications of method. It seems evident, however, that by his electrochemical process of decomposition Davy discovered potassium and sodium, as announced in his paper read Nov. 19, 1807. And that by his announcement of June 30, 1808 he was the discoverer of barium, strontium, calcium, and magnium, these by decomposition of the earths.

As early as 1806 Davy had concluded that "the combinations and decompositions by electricity were referable to the law of electrical attractions and repulsions; and advanced the hypothesis, that chemical and electrical attraction were produced by the same cause, acting in one case on particles, in the other on masses; and that the same property under different modifications, was the cause of all the phenomena

---

[9] *Ibid*.   [11] *Memoirs*, I, 174.
[10] Bakerian Lecture of 1806. *Memoirs*, I, 359.

exhibited by different voltaic combinations."[12] As supporting this hypothesis Davy pointed out "that heat, and sometimes heat and light, result from the exertion of both of electrical and chemical attractive powers." Also, bodies which on contact are positive to others are, when made more highly positive, rendered capable of greater powers of combination, "whereas, when they are placed in a state corresponding to the negative electrical state, their powers of union are destroyed."[13] He conceives of electrical and chemical changes as distinct phenomena but produced by the same power. Chemical changes are not, he says, occasioned by electrical changes.

There is evident in Davy's theory an effort to get at the common denominator of the various expressions of force—heat, light, chemical and electrical action. "The relations of bodies derived from their electrical powers, are coincident with those dependent upon their agencies in combustion."[14] Heated bodies affect each other at a distance. There is "radiant heat." "One solution of this phenomenon is, that particles are thrown off from heated bodies with great velocity, which by acting on our organs produce the sensations of heat or light."[15] The radiant matters emitted may be considered either as specific substances, or "the phenomena of radiation do, in fact, depend upon motions communicated to subtle matter everywhere in space."[16]

Herschel's discovery of the dark heat rays had, by the time of the publication of Davy's *Chemical Philosophy,* been confirmed by various good observers. "It is evident," says Davy, "that matter set in motion by the sun has the power of producing heat without light, and that its rays are less

[12] *Memoirs.* I, 325.
[13] Davy, *Chemical Philosophy,* 193.
[14] *Ibid.*
[15] *Ibid.,* 83.
[16] *Ibid.,* 83-4.

refrangible than the visible rays."[17]   That the moon's light is apparently without accompanying heat Davy discusses in a passage important as the possible key to difficult lines in *Prometheus* descriptive of the moon.   Pointing out that the brilliancy of the moon's light is to that of the sun as 1 to 300,000 and that the heat rays would be in the same ratio, Davy suggests also another explanation for the coldness of the moon's light: "It is possible that a greater number of the most heat making rays, than of the other rays, may be absorbed by that planet."[18]   If the rays are absorbed their motion must be "communicated to the particles of that body, but whether they adhere to it, or are thrown off in new aggregates, as radiant heat, cannot well be discussed, for we have no means accurate enough to determine whether in such cases there is an increase of weight."[19]

"In general, in nature, the effects of the solar rays are very compounded."[20]   Not only is the heat necessary to plant growth but certain chemical effects are due to the action of light.   Plants deprived of light lose their color; and in flowers the variety of hues is due to solar light.   Animals also require the sun's light, whose various effects "offer an analogy to the agencies of electricity."   Clearly, Davy in his theories relative to light, electricity, and radiant energy in general is in the Newtonian tradition.

Important to this synthesis are the experiments carried on by Davy and others with an electric charge passed through various gases and through a vacuum.   Of the two poles of an electric circuit "a vivid spot of white light is always perceived on the negative point and rays seem to diverge from the positive point."[21]   The difference between the appearance of the two points, Davy found, did not depend upon the nature

[17] *Ibid.*, 201.   [19] *Ibid.*, 221.   [21] *Ibid.*, 178.
[18] *Ibid.*, 203.   [20] *Ibid.*, 212.

of the intervening gas, for the effects in various gases were virtually the same. The spark, however, "will pass much farther through rarified air or light gases, than through dense air or heavy gases."[22]

When an electric discharge was made through rarified air the distance covered by the spark increased as the density decreased. In an approximate vacuum the discharges leaped six or seven inches, "producing a most beautiful corruscation of purple light, the charcoal became intensely lighted, and some platina wire attached to it, fused with brilliant scintillations, and fell in large globules upon the plate of the pump."[23] The resemblance of these effects to the corruscations of the Aurora Borealis inclines Davy to credit Franklin's hypothesis "that the Auroras may arise from a discharge of electricity, accumulated in the atmosphere near the poles, into its rarer parts; though other solutions of the phenomena may be given on the idea, that the earth itself is endowed with electrical polarity; or that the motions of the atmosphere produce the effect."[24]

After citing with approval Newton's hypothesis that light and common matter are perhaps convertible into each other, Davy remarks that we have yet "much to learn with respect to the affections and motions of radiant matter; and this subject when fully understood, promises to connect together chemical and mechanical science, and to offer new and more comprehensive views of the corpuscular arrangements of matter."[25] It is precisely, is it not, through its knowledge of radioactivity that modern science has come to its conclusions as to the nature of matter. Davy goes on to say:

In radiant matter, the particles act almost independently of the common laws of attraction; and by prismatic refraction the difference of their actions is determined, and it seems probable that

[22] Davy, *Chemical Philosophy*, 136.
[23] *Ibid.*, 153.   [24] *Ibid.*, 223.   [25] *Ibid.*, 223.

the relations of the different particles to the crystalline arrangements of matter, will be found connected with those powers which they possess analogous to electrical qualities.

If that sublime idea of the ancient Philosophers which has been sanctioned by the approbation of Newton, should be true, namely, that there is only one species of matter, the different chemical, as well as mechanical forms of which are owing to the different arrangement of its particles, then a method of analyzing those forms may probably be found in their relations to radiant matter.[26]

It asks greater knowledge of science and of the history of science than the writer of this survey possesses to show wherein, as based on the findings of his predecessors and contemporaries, Davy was justified in forecasts which so remarkably anticipate the discoveries and theories of a century later. If he was merely giving his imagination rein it bore him in a moment to a goal which experimental science reached only after decades of laborious effort. A few additional citations will make the degree of Davy's prescience apparent.

Remarking that "complexity almost always belongs to the early epochs of every science," Davy points out that already "a great part of the phenomena of chemistry may be submitted to calculation; and there is great reason to believe that at no very distant period the whole science will be capable of elucidation by mathematical principles."[27] Discoveries already made and analogies already inferred suggest a simplification of the agencies to which chemical phenomena are ascribed. "The more the phenomena of the universe are studied, the more distinct their connection appears, the more simple their causes, the more magnificent their design, and the more wonderful the wisdom and power of their Author."[28]

"The term element," Davy observes, "is used as synonymous with undecompounded body." The constantly altering technic of chemistry makes it uncertain what, if any, sub-

[26] *Ibid.*   [27] *Ibid.,* 59.   [28] *Ibid.*

stance is undecompoundable. "Matter may ultimately be found to be the same in essence, differing only in the arrangements of its particles; or two or three simple substances may produce all the varieties of compound bodies."[29]   He conceives it possible "that the same ponderable matter in different electrical states, or in different arrangements, may constitute substances chemically different: there are parallel cases in the different states in which bodies are found, connected with their different relations to temperature. . . .   Even if it should be ultimately found that oxygene and hydrogene are the same matter in different states of electricity, or that two or three elements in different proportions constitute all bodies, the great doctrines of chemistry, the theory of definite proportions, and the specific attractions of bodies must remain immutable."[30]   Those substances now considered primary would then be known as secondary, "but the numbers representing them would be the same, and they would probably be all found to be produced by the additions of multiples of some simple numbers or fractional parts."[31]

The advancement of chemical science tends, Davy concludes, to verify the hypotheses of the earliest great chemists and philosophers. "That the forms of natural bodies may depend upon different arrangements of the same particles of matter has been a favorite hypothesis advanced in the earliest era of physical research. . . .   This sublime chemical speculation sanctioned by the authority of Hooke, Newton, and Boscovich, must not be confounded with the ideas advanced by the alchemists concerning the convertibility of the elements into each other.   The possible transmutation of metals has generally been reasoned upon, not as a philosophical research, but as an empirical process."[32]

Even more explicitly formulative of an electrical theory

[29] Davy, *Chemical Philosophy,* 181.
[30] *Ibid.,* 487.   [31] *Ibid.*   [32] *Ibid.,* 487.

of matter which all but employs our modern terminology
is Davy's statement that "Whether matter consists of indivisible
corpuscles, or physical points endowed with attraction and
repulsion, still the same conclusions may be formed concerning the powers by which they act, and the quantities in which
they combine; and the powers seem capable of being measured
by their electrical relations, and the quantities on which they
act of being expressed by numbers."[33] Not only does Davy
conceive of matter as electrical, as "physical points endowed
with attraction and repulsion" but he thinks these particles to
be in motion about their axes. The passage should be cited
entire, as, more nearly than any other I have found, it concisely and clearly sets forth Davy's most radical theory and
justifies an interpretation which I shall later make of a difficult
passage in the *Prometheus:*

Since all matter may be made to fill a smaller volume by cooling, it is evident that the particles of matter must have space between them; and since every body can communicate the power of
expansion to a body of lower temperature, that is, can give an
expansive motion to its particles, it is a probable inference that its
own particles are possessed of motion; but as there is no change in
the position of its parts as long as its temperature is uniform, the
motion, if it exist, must be a vibratory or undulatory motion, or a
motion of the particles round their axes, or a motion of particles
round each other.[34]

This, I take it, is the ultimate of Davy's speculation. He
glances at the possibility of electricity being akin to vital
forces but unlike Erasmus Darwin is disinclined to place much
credence in it. After discussing the electrical properties of
the *gymnotus electricus* and the *torpedo* he remarks: "It has
been conceived that other phenomena of living action may
be connected with the operation of weak electrical powers;
such as secretion; and some ingenious hints on this subject

[33] *Ibid.,* 57.   [34] *Ibid.,* 95.

have been advanced by Dr. Wollaston and Mr. Howe, and some experiments relating to the subject instituted by Mr. Brande."[35] He deems such inquiries as "worthy of further pursuit. . . . but they must not be confounded with certain vague speculations, that have been advanced by some authors on the general dependence of nervous or sensitive action, and muscular or irritable action upon electricity; such speculations are mere associations of words derived from known phenomena, and applied illogically to unknown things. The laws of dead and living nature appear to be perfectly distinct; material powers are made subservient to the purposes of life, and the elements of matter are newly arranged in living organs; but they are merely the instruments of a superior principle."[36]

Perhaps it is scientific caution which makes Davy draw back before a speculation sanctioned by Newton; or perhaps it is an aversion to things mystical which prompts him. Davy, as revealed in the *Memoirs* by his brother, or in his note-books, seems sufficiently orthodox in his theology. An identification of force, matter, and the spirit of animation as electricity in its various manifestations leads either to a mechanistic philosophy or to Platonic mysticism. Davy seemingly wished to avoid either alternative. These concluding citations, while glancing at a doctrine of reincarnation and clearly evolutionary in essence, are rather more in the vein of the conventional pulpit utterance expressive of man's mental prostration in the presence of the infinite:

Probably there is an analogy in all existence. . . . In the planetary system it is probable man will be found connected with a higher intellectual nature, and it is possible that the *monad*, or soul, is constantly undergoing a series of progressions.[37]

[35] Davy, *Chemical Philosophy*, 174.
[36] *Ibid.*
[37] *Memoirs*, II, 69. Quoted from Davy's note-books.

Again:

Is there not a monad, or one perceptive atom or principle, which plays, as it were, round different arrangements in the brain, and which acts in its own little world, as the great diffusive monad does in the universe? But how far beyond our power of conception![38]

Davy's value to Shelley lies, I believe, in those aspects of his thought which I have endeavored to illustrate: his work with nitrous oxide; his interest in radiation and the dark rays; his stress upon electricity as the chief agent among the forces which operate in the creation of new soils and compounds that restore the wastage due to erosion; and, chief, Davy's conception of matter as electrical force, as particles of electricity revolving in minute systems, though seemingly at rest. This conception I believe to be also Shelley's and to be definitely expounded in a notable passage in *Prometheus*.

Davy, as I have pointed out, in one particular, in this demonstration of the electrical nature of matter, pushes Newton's theory to the more explicit conclusions made possible by the advances in chemistry and electricity since Newton's time. But Newton's mystical synthesis of force, matter, and the spirit of animation, Davy rejects. Here Shelley follows Newton as being reconcilable with Plato. For Davy's rather timid acceptance of conventional theology Shelley could at no time have had any use.

[38] *Ibid.*, 74.

CHAPTER VIII

PROMETHEUS UNBOUND:
ELECTRICITY THE SPIRIT OF THE EARTH

THE IMPORTANCE of electrical phenomena in the scientific speculations of Shelley's day has been evident in the chapters devoted to Erasmus Darwin and Humphry Davy. Newton's theory of the ether, in which that supposititious medium was likened to electricity, has also been noted. Further to indicate the range and multiplicity of electrical experimentation and theory during the eighteenth century is hardly necessary to my purpose. The modern reader previously unfamiliar with the field will be amazed at the extent of the literature available. Priestley, writing a history of electrical theory and knowledge in the year 1775, gives a casual and partial bibliography of forty or fifty volumes in four languages. In the decades that follow, the transactions of scientific societies overflow with papers upon innumerable electrical themes. As always in the early days of science, the reader with the perspective of a hundred years is surprised to discover how modern many of the more daring speculations are and how early even practical inventions, such, for instance, as the telegraph, were experimentally anticipated, though not, in their first forms, made commercially available.

Among the experimenters and theorists into whose work I have gone, in addition to the scientists already discussed, Father Giambatista Beccaria is the most important for my purpose. In his essay upon "Terrestrial Atmospheric Electricity During Serene Weather" is to be found the key to Shelley's identification of the Spirit of the Earth in *Prometheus* with atmospheric electricity. Father Beccaria's work, *A Treatise upon Artificial Electricity* in which he included the essay upon Atmospheric Electricity is published in one volume in English translation, London, 1776. An excellent summary of his work appears much later in *Nicholson's Journal* of Feb. 1813 (vol. 34), when interest in the subject was revived after work similar to his had been done by other experimenters. Whether Shelley was attracted to Beccaria's work by this article or happened independently upon it, or whether later in Italy he read Beccaria's work in Italian, there is no certain means of knowing. But from the accuracy with which he employs certain of Beccaria's findings it seems probable that he had the work freshly in mind at the time he wrote *Prometheus Unbound*.

Shelley's poem *The Cloud* should in this connection be noted. It was one of the shorter pieces published with *Prometheus Unbound* in 1820; and in the light of Shelley's employment of atmospheric phenomena in the longer poem seems unmistakably a by-product to or, even, in a sense the key to *Prometheus*. That *The Cloud* is an excellent piece of meteorology has long been noted. Its derivation from Beccaria's work is, I think, evident. The same phenomena are treated, and Shelley, for all the poetry of his expression, is accurate in his science. The following excerpt from Beccaria will serve both to express concisely the general theme of his scientific experiments and to suggest, possibly, the specific inspiration of Shelley's *The Cloud*. Certainly the poem is scarcely more than the poetic rendition of the same body of facts:

> With regard to atmospheric electricity it appears manifest, that Nature makes an extensive use of it for promoting vegetation. I. In the spring, when plants begin to grow, *temporary* and electric clouds begin to appear, and pour frequent electric rains; the electricity of clouds, and of rain, increases afterwards in summer, and continues to do so, till that part of Autumn in which the last

fruits are gathered; so that it appears, that the electricity which obtains in clouds and rain, when carried to a certain degree, serves to promote, with regard to vegetation, the effects of common heat.

II. It even seems that electricity successively supplies common heat itself, with that moisture, by the help of which it actuates and animates vegetation; which, if heat acted alone, would inevitably be stopped. In fact, it is the electric fire that gathers the vapours together, forms clouds with them, and afterwards dissolves them into rain: it is the same fire, therefore, that supplies the earth with the nutritive moisture which is necessary to plants; and this moisture, by melting the saline particles it meets with, by diffusing them along with itself into the inmost pores of plants, causes them to grow and vegetate with such admirable incomprehensible regularity.

III. The common saying of countrymen, *that no kind of watering gives the country so smiling a look as rain,* may be explained on the same principle. The rainy clouds, by extending their own electric atmospheres to plants, dispose the pores of the latter to receive with greater facility, the liquid which is soon to follow; and the succeeding drops penetrate into them the better, as everyone carries along with it a portion of the penetrating dilating element.[1]

The expression "dissolves them into rain" is the probable origin of Shelley's line

> Whilst he is dissolving in rains

And the function of the electricity as pilot in the poem and even the use of the scientific word "pores" are both reminiscent of Beccaria.

Beccaria's investigations have to do with the degree of electricity in the atmosphere under all atmospheric conditions, of serene weather, day and night. He ran up exploring wires, invented electrometers and hygrometers, and kept a careful record of his results. These may be briefly summarized to some such effect as this: The atmospheric electricity during

[1] Beccaria, *Artificial Electricity,* 286.

serene weather is virtually always of the excessive or positive kind. Drawn with the water vapor from the earth by the sun, this electricity ceases to be active, having reached its maximum, about mid-day. At the close of the day it declines, being precipitated in dew or frost and at dawn has wholly returned to the earth or persists in the atmosphere to but a slight degree. Winds and clouds and the degree of moisture in the air modify these generalizations somewhat. Any disturbing factor may precipitate the atmospheric electricity, as in a high wind or thunder storm. Usually, however, the quiet round of electric action proceeds as depicted, and it is these simple phenomena which Shelley clothes in poetic imagery in *Prometheus.*

Erasmus Darwin now enters the picture. In the *Botanic Garden,* it may be recalled, the activities of Nymphs, Sylphs, Salamanders and Gnomes are celebrated; these 'genii' being the symbols or personifications of the physical and chemical activities in the various realms of nature. "Effulgent Maids" are evoked in one passage and their round of duties is described. These duties dramatize various phosphoric and electrical phenomena. Let me cite from Darwin:

> Effulgent Maids! You round deciduous day,
> Tressed with soft beams, your glittering bands array;
> On Earth's cold bosom, as the Sun retires,
> Confine with folds of air the lingering fires;
> O'er Eve's pale forms diffuse phosphoric light,
> And deck with lambent flames the shrine of Night.
> So, warm'd and kindled by meridian skies,
> And view'd in darkness with dilated eyes,
> Bologna's chalks with faint ignition blaze
> Beccari's shells emit prismatic rays.
>
> *Botanic Garden,* I. ll. 173-182.

You with light Gas the lamps nocturnal feed
Which dance and glimmer o'er the marshy mead;

Shine round Calendula at twilight hours,
And tip with silver all her saffron flowers;
Warm on her mossy couch the radiant Worm,
Guard from cold dews her love-illumin'd form,
From leaf to leaf conduct the virgin light,
Star of the earth, and diamond of the night.
You hid in air the tropic Beetle burn,
And fill with golden flame his winged urn;
Or gild the surge with insect-sparks, that swarm
Round the bright oar, the kindling prow alarm;
Or arm in waves, electric in his ire,
The dread Gymnotus with ethereal fire.

Ibid., I. ll. 189-202.

Briefly to run over Darwin's annotations of this passage will serve to show the unity of theme underlying it. All these phenomena have to do with phosphorescent or electric effects which, again, may be considered as similar if not identical. The "phosphoric light" which is diffused "o'er Eve's pale forms," says Darwin, "may be owing to the phosphorescent quality (as it is called) of almost all bodies; that is, when they have been exposed to the sun, they continue to emit light for a considerable time afterwards." The chalks, the "Bolognian stone," are a selenite or gypsum "long celebrated for its phosphorescent quality." The shells of Beccari (not Beccaria but another Italian scientist) allude to experiments in phosphoric light conducted by that investigator with certain calcareous compositions. But what of the association of phosphorescence with electricity?

That phosphorescence, whether due to decay or other causes, is associated with electricity is the hypothesis of Davy in the following excerpt taken from a speculation upon the nature of light, chemical action, and electricity as three allied manifestations of a single elemental force:

Many phenomena which have been attributed to combined light, appear to be electrical, or to be merely the effect of the ignition of the substances, for whenever heat arises beyond a certain degree, bodies become luminous; pieces of quartz rubbed together are rendered electrical; and by percussion or friction any hard bodies may be intensely heated.

During the putrefaction of certain animal and vegetable substances, light is emitted; and this is no more difficult to account for, than the heat produced during similar operations.

The light emitted by certain living insects, appears to depend upon the secretion of a substance very easy of decomposition; and any chemical change may be supposed adequate to the production of light.[2]

Further confirmation of this association of phosphorescent and electric light is found in a passage from Beccaria:

I . . . betook myself to make experiments on the numerous class of phosphoreous bodies, enumerated by my respected friend, Signor Beccari, in the *Comentari Bolognesi,* and was soon enabled to answer Dr. Franklin, that the phosphoreity of the electric light was the same with that of the solar light.[3]

A few lines below the description of "Bologna's Chalks" in the poetic passage cited from Darwin, occur the words "insect-sparks that swarm round the bright oar." The allusion is clearly to the phosphorescent phenomena of tropic seas. One of Darwin's Additional Notes elucidates:

In some seas, as particularly about the coast of Malabar, as a ship floats along, it seems during the night to be surrounded with fire, and to leave a long tract of light behind it. Whenever the sea is gently agitated it seems converted into little stars, every drop as it breaks emits light, like bodies electrified in the dark. Mr. Bomare says, that when he was at the port of Cettes in Languedoc, and bathing with a companion in the sea after a very hot day, they both appeared covered with fire after every immersion, and that

---

[2] Davy, *Elements of Chemical Philosophy,* 221.
[3] Beccaria, *Artificial Electricity,* 323.

laying his wet hand on the arm of his companion, who had not then dipped himself, the exact mark of his hand and fingers were seen in characters of fire. As numerous microscopic insects are found in this shining water, its light has been generally ascribed to them, though it seems probable that fish-slime in hot countries may become in such a state of incipient putrefaction as to give light, especially when by agitation it is more exposed to the air; otherwise it is not easy to explain why agitation should be necessary to produce this marine light.[4]

Immediately after the lines descriptive of the phosphorescent sea occurs the reference to the "dread Gymnotus electric in his ire." Clearly in Darwin's mind the phenomena of phosphorescence and electricity are, if not identical, closely related.

What now of the light Gas that feeds the nocturnal lamps? Darwin alludes here, he informs us in a note, to the *"ignis fatuus* or Jack a lantern" which "is supposed to originate from the inflammable air, or Hydrogene, given up from morasses; which being of a heavier kind from its impurity than that obtained from iron and water, hovers near the surface of the earth, and uniting with common air gives out light by its slow ignition." Darwin does not, in the note, ascribe an electric origin to the ignition of the gas, but this is elsewhere done in contemporary works of science.

Several meteors seen in the atmosphere have been suspected to be the effects of inflammable air fired by electricity. The weak lightnings, without any explosion, that are sometimes observed near the horizon in serene weather, especially in hot climates, are considered, by a very judicious philosopher, to be nothing more than inflammable air [hydrogen] detached from the earth by the heat, etc. and fired by electricity, or by some other unknown cause. Mr. Volta of Como supposes, that the *ignes fatui* are occasioned by the inflammable air which proceeds from marshy grounds, and is

---

[4] *Botanic Garden,* Additional Note IX.

set on fire by electric sparks. Those meteors called *falling stars,* he supposes to be fired by the same means.[5]

Of the remaining lines the "radiant Worm" is the glow worm, again a phenomenon of phosphorescent origin, and the light of Calendula likewise.

If, side by side with the passage from Darwin, be put the lines from the beginning of scene 4, Act III of *Prometheus* descriptive of the Spirit of the Earth, certain similarities will be at once obvious:

> *Ione* (speaking of the Spirit of the Earth)
> Sister it is not earthly; how it glides
> Under the leaves! how on its head there burns
> A light like a green star, whose emerald beams
> Are twined with its fair hair! how, as it moves,
> The splendor drops in flakes upon the grass!
> Knowest thou It?
> >   *Panthea*
> >   It is the delicate spirit
> That guides the earth through heaven. From afar
> The populous constellations call that light
> The loveliest of the planets; and sometimes
> It floats along the spray of the salt sea,
> Or makes its chariot of a foggy cloud,
> Or walks through fields or cities while men sleep,
> Or o'er the mountain tops, or down the rivers,
> Or through the green waste wilderness, as now,
> Wondering at all it sees. Before Jove reigned
> It loved our sister Asia, and it came
> Each leisure hour to drink the liquid light
> Out of her eyes, for which it said it thirsted
> As one bit by a dipsas. . . .
> >   *P. U.* III. 4. ll. 1-19.

The third line of this passage

A light like a green star, whose emerald beams . . .

[5] Cavallo, *Treatise on Air and Other Elastic Fluids,* 647 (1781).

is curiously similar in its imagery to the lines in Darwin

> . . . the virgin light
> Star of the earth and diamond of the night.

The likeness of the light is to a diamond in the one and to an emerald in the other and in both occurs the word 'star'. Now in Beccaria's discussion of electrical effects the metaphor of the star receives a particular emphasis as the following citation will attest:

In general this law of indication consists in the difference of the appearances exhibited by the electric fire, when issuing from a blunted point of metal placed in such situations that the electrical fire may, according to the theory, issue from one of the systems and pass into the other. If the point has been annexed to that of the systems from which the fire *issues* and is properly directed towards a plain portion of the surface of the other, then the fire assumes an appearance that I have distinguished by the appellation of a *brush;* but when the point is annexed to the system into which the fire *enters,* then the fire assumes another appearance, to which I have given the name of *little star.*[6]

Let me indulge in a bit of hypothetical reconstruction of Shelley's mental processes and seek to guess the associations aroused in his mind by the word 'star' as thus employed by Beccaria. The word is beautifully descriptive of the effect of electric light at one terminal of a Leyden jar, with whose effects Shelley was familiar. If the terminals in the jar are of copper or silver, the color of the light is green. Thus we have in Shelley's lines the "green star" with its "emerald beams"; and the splendor which "drops in flakes," is likewise descriptive of the corruscations of an electric terminal as, too, reminiscent of Coleridge's lines

> And when they reared, the elfish light
> Fell off in hoary flakes.

[6] Beccaria, *Artificial Electricity,* 38.

In the *Ancient Mariner* the lines are descriptive of the sea-snakes swimming in a phosphorescent sea.

Phosphorescent and electrical associations cluster about the "star." If we assume for the moment, what is likely enough, that Shelley, reading Beccaria, was much taken by his account of the activities of atmospheric electricity and thought to make poetic use of them, the "star" may have been the association which recalled Darwin's similar use of the atmospheric phenomena of light, electrical and phosphorescent in their nature, in the passage from the *Botanic Garden* which I have quoted. Darwin's work, in my hypothesis, Shelley had read some years before, and in the passage from *Prometheus* descriptive of the Spirit of the Earth, the resemblances to Darwin are unconscious. Let me point out the similarity of the phenomena described in the two passages and demonstrate that in Shelley, as in Darwin, atmospheric electricity may be made to account for them.

The Spirit, on whose head is the green light, guides the earth through heaven, of which figure of speech more in a later connection. Note the forms or vehicles in which it manifests itself: first it floats in the spray of the salt sea, to which, tentatively, may be assigned the interpretation of phosphorescence, as in Darwin's lines descriptive of the "insect-sparks" around the "bright oar."

Or makes its chariot of a foggy cloud.

The following passage from Beccaria explains the electrical character of fogs.

Low and thick fogs (especially when in their rising, they find the air above them pretty free from moisture) carry up to the exploring wire, when they reach it, an electricity which becomes manifested by frequent little sparks.[7]

[7] *Ibid.*, 440.

The next lines are:

> Or walks through fields or cities while men sleep
> Or o'er the mountain tops, or down the rivers,
> Or through the green waste wilderness. . . .

The most plausible interpretation of these allusions is that in the first, and probably in the third, line the *ignis fatuus,* or will o' the wisp, is meant as in Darwin's lines. That electric properties were supposed to pertain to it was shown in the citation from Cavallo, which, too, if the second line of the verse, "o'er the mountain-tops," etc., refers to shooting stars, meteors, and such phenomena, supplies also a gloss upon it. Will o' the wisp, shooting stars, and meteors are all supposedly electrical phenomena.

Further lines descriptive of the visual appearance of the Spirit are:

> I hid myself
> Within a fountain in the public square,
> Where I lay like the reflex of the moon
> Seen in a wave under green leaves. . . .
>
> *P. U.* III. 4. ll. 61-64.

Broken moon-lit water would be phosphorescent to the eye and therefore a suitable hiding place for the phosphorescent (or electric) spirit.

Our supposition that the Spirit is phosphorescent and electric is thus far buttressed by two arguments, first the parallels to the lines in Darwin which, from his own notes, are thus to be interpreted; second by the citations from other scientific writings (Cavallo and Beccaria) which elucidate lines not strictly paralleled in Darwin. What then of the passage in which the Spirit runs to Asia and addresses her as Mother?

Mrs. Shelley's notes to *Prometheus* identify Asia as one of the Oceanides, and "according to other mythological interpretations, the same as Venus and Nature." Asia is the wife of Prometheus, to be reunited to him in the day of his liberation, typifying the mystical union of man and nature. I have no wish at this point, nor indeed in this book, more than to touch upon the allegorical or symbolical nature of *Prometheus*. To do so effectively demands a consideration of all the complicated strands of this difficult poem. It suffices, however, in this instance to point out that the conception of atmospheric electricity as the child of earth and as returning to its mother is strictly in harmony with Beccaria's thesis that atmospheric electricity is drawn from the earth by the sun in water vapor and returns to its source in rain, dew, frost, and lightning.

The next lines fully support this interpretation:

> May I then play beside thee the long noons,
> When work is none in the bright silent air?
> > *P. U.* III. 4. ll. 28-9.

At noon, according to Beccaria, the atmospheric electricity, having reached the point of saturation, is quiescent provided the day is serene and windless. Two citations will sufficiently prove the point and make Shelley's meaning clear.

In the morning, according as the sun rises higher, the electricity, whether it began before sun-rise, or only after, gradually increases. This gradual increase of the morning electricity begins sooner, according as the hygrometer continues, after sun-rise, to indicate a higher degree of dryness, and as such dryness more speedily increases. These increased both intensity and frequency of the electricity last, in serene days, in which no impetuous wind takes place, so long as the sun does not draw near the place of its setting, and the hygrometer keeps near the highest degree which it had reached. When the sun is near its setting, and in proportion as the hygrometer begins to retreat, the intensity of the daily electricity lessens, and its frequency increases.[8]

[8] Beccaria, *Atmospheric Electricity*, 454.

And:

On the 23d of June, the hygrometer, from −5 rose to −17.3; which denoted great dryness, for the 22d had been exceedingly wet, and I have constantly observed that one day is not sufficient to carry the hygrometer quite up to the actual degree of dryness, if the dampness was very great before. Conformably to the above great rise of the hygrometer, the electricity which, at 7 in the morning, was at zero, at 8:30 had risen to 6° and during the whole day kept at 80° or very near. On the evening at 6, the electricity had fallen to 5°; between 8 and 9, it fell to 2°; at 10 o'clock it rose again to 5°, but it soon lowered again to 3°, to 2°, and there it remained till I ceased to observe, that is till 11.25.[9]

Additional verification of Beccaria may be found in De Luc and De Saussure.[10]

There are other lines in *Prometheus* which verify the interpretation given. Quiescent atmospheric electricity is clearly meant in the figure:

> Like veiled lightning asleep.

Again the Spirit of the Hour in describing the flight of his coursers which "are fed with the lightning" says

> Ere the cloud piled on Atlas can dwindle
> We encircle the earth and the moon
> We shall rest from long labors at noon.
>
> *P. U.* II. 4. ll. 171-173.

The last line is in harmony with the

> long noons
> When work is none in the bright silent air.

And a further passage is made intelligible by Beccaria's observation that at dawn atmospheric electricity is either non

---

[9] Beccaria, *Atmospheric Electricity*, 457.

[10] In an article by J. A. De Luc in *Nicholson's Journal*, Vol. 36 (1813) quotations are made from De Saussure which tally with Beccaria's earlier work; Beccaria is not mentioned, though the apparatus employed was similar to his.

existent or at its lowest ebb. The coursers "fed with the lightning" respire at dawn and rest at noon.

> On the brink of the night and the morning
> My coursers are wont to respire;
> But the Earth has just whispered a warning
> That their flight must be swifter than fire;
>
> *P. U.* II. 5. ll. 1-4.

These same coursers "fed with the lightning" drink also "of the whirlwind's stream," a line whose meaning becomes apparent and in harmony with the interpretation of its companion line when it is recalled that electrical effects accompany the action of the whirlwind or simoon. The fact is mentioned by Darwin, Davy, and Cavallo.

> In the West Indies the sea rises like a cone in the whirl, and is met by black clouds . . . the upper and lower airs exchange their plus or minus electricity in perpetual lightnings.[11]

The Spirit of the Earth is described as returning to play beside Asia in the long noons, to "hide my eyes in thy soft arms." In the lines from a previous passage Panthea says of it:

> It loved our sister Asia, and it came
> Each leisure hour to drink the liquid light
> Out of her eyes, for which it said it thirsted
> As one bit by a dipsas.

The electrical interpretation gives the passage explicit meaning. The atmospheric electricity derives from, renews itself from, the earth. In an earlier passage the same idea is expressed but with an additional implication. The Earth speaks of the Spirit of the Earth and addresses Asia:

[11] Darwin, *Botanic Garden*, Additional Note XXXIII. Also, Davy, *Elements of Chemical Philosophy*, 141; Tiberius Cavallo, *The Elements of Natural or Experimental Philosophy*, II, 305. (London, 1803). Cavallo observes that the electrical phenomena "appear to be rather the necessary consequence than the cause of the water spout."

> This is my torch-bearer;
> Who let his lamp out in old time with gazing
> On eyes from which he kindled it anew
> With love, which is as fire, sweet daughter mine,
> For such is that within thine own.
>
> *P. U.* III. 3. ll. 148-152.

The identification of love with electricity is clear. Again, Prometheus speaks

> . . . I wandered once
> With Asia, drinking life from her loved eyes.
>
> *P. U.* I. ll. 122-123.

The identification of life, love, and electricity is implicit also in other passages:

> . . . Love
> That planet-crested Shape swept by on lightning-braided pinions,
> Scattering the liquid joy of life from his ambrosial tresses.
> His footsteps paved the world with light.
>
> *P. U.* I. ll. 763-768.

The passages descriptive of Asia repeat the same theme. She is the source of love and energy. She is radiant and life giving:

> Sister of her [Asia] whose footsteps pave the world
> With loveliness. . . .
>
> *P. U.* II. 1. ll. 68-9.

Of her it is said:

> . . . love, like the atmosphere
> Of the sun's fire filling the living world,
> Burst from thee, and illumined earth and heaven
> And the deep ocean and the sunless caves
> And all that dwells within them.
>
> *P. U.* II. 5. ll. 26-30.

In the Indian vale where Asia awaits Prometheus, the scene once desolate and frozen is made beautiful by "the ether of

her transforming presence." Her increasing radiance fore-
tells the liberation of Prometheus. She is described as "Life of
Life." Her smiles "make the cold air fire." She is the "Lamp
of Earth," too bright to be gazed upon. Similar is the description of the transformed world when Prometheus is freed:

> . . . the impalpable thin air
> And the all-circling sunlight were transformed,
> As if the sense of love, dissolved in them,
> Had folded itself round the sphered world.
> P. U. III. 4. ll. 100-103.

The identification of love, energy, and the spirit of animation in Shelley's imagery need not be further stressed. I believe it to be self-evident. Nor is it without scientific justification in the speculations of Newton and Erasmus Darwin as
I have shown previously. Davy, it was noted, was cautious
in ascribing an electrical character to the spirit of animation
but believed the subject to be worthy investigation. In Beccaria
there are to be found speculations linking electricity with bodily
functions:

> Why should not the strong perpetual friction exercised by the
> blood against the venal, or arterial vessels, also excite electricity?
> Why should not a small globule of blood, while it rubs against a
> given part of an artery, diffuse into it some of its own electric fire,
> or receive some new portion from the same? . . . I really think,
> that such a perpetual excitation, as mentioned above, both takes
> place, and produces very beneficial effects, in the animal economy.[12]

In another passage upon the phenomena of vision and of
phosphoreity Beccaria ascribes electrical properties to the sense
of sight:

> The duration of *vision,* otherwise that lasting impression made
> on our optic nerves by external objects, which continues to be felt
> though the objects themselves are removed, may also, I think, be

[12] Beccaria, *Artificial Electricity,* 288.

explained by the phosphoreity, which is found to be proper to electric light, as well as to common light; so that the electric fluid harboured in the substance of the organs of sight, and vibrated by any light whatever, produces that durable sensation we mention, in the same manner as if it were produced by the action of common light.[13]

A paper read before the Royal Society in 1816[14] recounts experiments made on the Torpedo, the fish which gives electric shocks. It was found that when shocks were frequently provoked the animal soon died; that when the electric organs were divided and the fish lost its power of giving shocks it was not exhausted. The conclusion was that the electric discharge was a vital function and that a most intimate relation existed between the nervous system and the electric organs.

Other experiments of the time with regard to galvanism are of the same general tenor. A paper reported in *Nicholson's Journal* for May, 1803 has to do with "experiments tending to ascertain the existence of two fluids in the animal economy, the one positive and the other negative, which, by their union appear to produce the agency of vitality." A letter of Volta to the same journal, Feb. 1802, gives "an account of experiments by which I demonstrate, in a convincing manner, what I have always maintained, namely that the pretended agent, or *galvanic fluid,* is nothing but common electrical fluid." In an article on Galvanism in Rees's *Cyclopedia* (1819) occurs the following passage:

It appears that Galvani, at the time of his discovery [the electrical phenomena arising from the chemical agency of certain metals with different fluids], was enthusiastic in the application of electrical theory to animal economy; and when he found the metallic

[13] Beccaria, *Artifiicial Electricity,* 288.

[14] *Abstracts of the Papers Printed in The Philosophical Transactions of the Royal Society of London,* II, 36. (1815-1830).

substances were capable of exciting muscular motion, he was confirmed in the opinion, that the inherent electricity of the animal was transmitted from the nerves to the muscles by the metals employed. Had this opinion been generally received, in all probability this subject would not have received much improvement.[15]

From this I gather that the vitality-electricity theory which had earlier excited considerable interest was, by the year 1819, in disrepute, at least insofar as the phenomena of galvanism were supposed to lend it credence.

I may remark that one of the most difficult points of this study is to determine how up-to-date Shelley's science was and its general soundness. Clearly scientific fact and, even more, scientific speculation enter into his philosophy. But it is apparent, also, that his imagination seizes upon theories which conservative scientists of his day distrusted. This fact does not necessarily mean that Shelley's imaginings are unsound. His ultimate position may be near the truth as we now apprehend it or as the innovations of science may tomorrow demonstrate it to be. That the spirit of animation is electrical or "ethereal" is, I take it, as much a guess today as in his time and much less a theme to engage the serious attention of a biologist.

Experimental use of galvanism and electricity in the treatment of disease seems also to have been more or less prevalent in Shelley's time. One of Shelley's boyish experiments was in the use of electricity for his sister's chilblains, a notion he must have derived from some similar employment of the wonder working "fluid." *Nicholson's Journal* for May, 1803, reports the use of galvanism to restore a paralyzed optic nerve; also its use in the case of a man bitten by a mad dog who thought himself contracting hydrophobia. The severity of the treatment led the patient to abandon his hallucination.

[15] Rees's *Cyclopedia,* article on Galvanism.

And there is record, also, of the use of electricity in the treatment of sciatica.

There are a host of images employed in *Prometheus* which are electrical in their nature, but many are sufficiently obvious and require no gloss, as thus:

> It tears me as fire tears a thunder-cloud.
>
> *P. U.* I. l. 255.

Others, perhaps, may profitably be commented on.

> As lightning tingles, hovering ere it strike.
>
> *P. U.* I. l. 134.

I take it that this refers to the zig-zag character of the electric flash through air. Passages in Beccaria explain the phenomenon:

> Air opposes sparks in proportion to its own density, and in proportion to the thickness of the stratum, through which the latter are led to pass.[16]
>
> Do not these facts render it manifest, that the zig-zag directions of sparks chiefly arise from the reaction of the air, against them?[17]

Beccaria's experiments with electric discharges in a vacuum showed that the discharge was steady and straight in the degree to which the air was rarefied.

The lines, typical of Shelley's constant employment of images relating to clouds, dew, and kindred phenomena

> As the fawn draws the hound
> As the lightning the vapor.
>
> *P. U.* II. 3. l. 65-6.

involve in their explanation the whole theory of cloud formation current in his time. The following excerpts from an article by Richard Kirwan, F. R. S. may suffice to put the matter intelligibly in small compass.

[16] Beccaria, *Artificial Electricity*, 232.
[17] *Ibid.*, 245.

Rain is the immediate result of the union of the particles which form clouds; and this union is the consequence of the subtraction of the electric atmospheres which keep them at a distance from each other; and this subtraction is itself the consequence either of the superior attraction of better conductors or of the attraction or repulsion of other clouds . . . and the result of their incorporation is the increased volume of their constituent particles. . . . When the attraction takes place between clouds differently and highly electrified, and within what electricians call the striking distance, the electric fluid is set free, the coalescence of the nubilous particles is more rapid and complete, and hence the large drops that follow flashes of lightning, or even floods, where the quantities both of vapour and electron are considerable, as between the tropics.[18]

One further instance and I shall conclude this aspect of the subject. In the first act of *Prometheus* the *Voice from the Springs* says

Thunderbolts had parched our water.

P. U. I. l. 78.

The phenomenon is remarked in Pliny:

We have accounts of many different kinds of thunderstorms. Those which are dry do not burn objects, but dissipate them. There is a third kind, which is called bright lightning, of a very wonderful nature, by which casks are emptied, without the vessels themselves being injured, or there being any other trace left of their operation.[19]

The same phenomenon is described in Beccaria, who speaks of an electric fire which will "even explode water into vapor,"[20] and again of "the violent explosion of liquids effected by lightning."[21]

The chapter may appropriately end upon a quotation from *Prometheus* which, in the light of the preceding discussion,

[18] *Nicholson's Journal*, June 1803, p. 120.
[19] Pliny, Book II, Chapter 52.
[20] Beccaria, *Artificial Electricity*, 253.
[21] *Ibid.*, 257.

asks no annotation, but which attests Shelley's interest in and knowledge of atmospheric phenomena:

> As the warm ether of the morning sun
> Wraps ere it drinks some cloud of wandering dew.
> I saw not, heard not, moved not, only felt
> His presence flow and mingle through my blood
> Till it became his life, and his grew mine,
> And I was thus absorbed, until it passed,
> And like the vapours when the sun sinks down,
> Gathering again in drops upon the pines,
> And tremulous as they, in the deep night
> My being was condensed; . . .
>
> > *P. U.* II. 1, ll. 77-86.

CHAPTER IX

PROMETHEUS UNBOUND: ELECTRICAL THEORY OF MATTER

THE LYRICAL fourth act of *Prometheus* complicates the study of the poem as a whole, not only in its larger interpretation, a phase of its study which we do not enter upon save in a most general way, but also by the introduction of scientific ideas much greater in scope than those of the first three acts. Mrs. Shelley's words should be weighed:

Shelley develops, more particularly in the lyrics of this drama, his abstruse and imaginative theories with regard to the Creation. It requires a mind as subtle and penetrating as his own to understand the mystic meanings scattered throughout the poem. They elude the ordinary reader by their abstraction and delicacy of distinction, but they are far from vague.

The fourth act is chiefly lyrical and it is in it that, in accordance with Mrs. Shelley's observation, some of the poet's subtlest scientific allusions are to be traced. Many of Shelley's meanings are, I believe, in the light of the historical sketch I have given, readily intelligible and will so appear. Others are difficult though decipherable. And there are some for which all I can do is to advance several possible solutions or guesses more or less plausible. The initial difficulty, the reconciliation of the Spirit of the Earth in the first three acts with the Spirit of the Earth depicted as the child asleep within the translucent sphere in the fourth, is not insuperable.

The fourth act was, we know, an afterthought. In it Shelley depicts the joy of a liberated universe. The forces of nature, twisted to maleficent ends by the evil will of Jupiter, are now free to work beneficently at man's behest. Shelley considers natural forces, some of whose powers he had before depicted, now much more comprehensively than in the first three acts. The Spirit of the Earth, previously identified with atmospheric electricity, becomes the symbol of more complicated forces. Its electrical implications remain but are enlarged; and through it, in a most notable passage, Shelley sets forth his fundamental notions of the nature of matter and energy, notions which, as we should anticipate, are in keeping with the speculations of Newton and Davy.

The heart of the matter lies in Panthea's long description of the sphere which "rushes with loud and whirlwind harmony" through an opening in the wood. The sphere is minutely described and then the child asleep within it, the Spirit of the Earth. The details descriptive of the sphere should be expressive of its nature. But they are very curious. Either Shelley is indulging in a flight of visual fancy, or, packed within these lines, are recondite meanings. The latter, in view of his employment of atmospheric electricity and of other scientific facts which can be demonstrated, is the more likely. These are the lines which seem to be the most significant:

> A sphere, which is as many thousand spheres;
> Solid as crystal, yet through all its mass
> Flow, as through empty space, music and light;
> Ten thousand orbs involving and involved,
> Purple and azure, white, green and golden,
> Sphere within sphere; and every space between
> Peopled with unimaginable shapes,
> Such as ghosts dream dwell in the lampless deep;
> Yet each inter-transpicuous; and they whirl
> Over each other with a thousand motions,
> Upon a thousand sightless axles spinning,
> And with the force of self-destroying swiftness,
> Intensely, slowly, solemnly, roll on . . .
> With mighty whirl the multitudinous orb,
> Grinds the bright brook into an azure mist
> Of elemental subtlety, like light; . . .

Round its intense yet self-conflicting speed
Seem kneaded into one aerial mass.
                                        P. U. IV. ll. 238-260.

The "sphere which is as many thousand spheres" becomes
more intelligible if we again invoke, as in a previous instance,
the aid of Erasmus Darwin and cite two passages of which I
believe Shelley's lines to be unconsciously reminiscent. In the
Botanic Garden, it will be recalled, the Goddess surveys the
Sylphs, Salamanders, Nymphs, and Gnomes which are the
personified activities of the four elements, earth, air, fire, and
water in the Rosicrucian nomenclature. Elements of air and
earth are thus described:

> The Goddess paused, admired with conscious pride
> The effulgent legions marshal'd by her side,
> Forms sphered in fire with trembling light array'd
> Ens without weight, and substance without shade.
>   *Botanic Garden,* I. ll. 421-424.

> And now the Goddess with attention sweet
> Turns to the Gnomes, that circle round her feet;
> Orb within orb approach the marshal'd trains
> And pygmy legions darken all the plains.
>   *Ibid.,* II. ll. 1-4.

In Darwin, as in Shelley, both "orbs" and "spheres" appear.
And in Shelley, as in Darwin, the mysterious spheres or orbs
are involved one within another in a fashion difficult to reconcile with any conception of "solid" matter. Here Darwin's
evident meaning throws light on the more obscure meaning
of Shelley. Darwin is advancing a concept of matter which
identifies matter with energy. The "ens without weight and
substance without shade," the "forms sphered in fire" can
mean nothing if not descriptive of units of matter which are
no more than radiant points of force.

It was evident in the review of Newton's and Davy's concepts of matter and force that advanced speculation in Shelley's day had anticipated theories which most of us no doubt consider very modern indeed. I pointed out wherein Davy seemed to be on the verge of defining matter in terms almost identical with those employed today. Let me repeat from Davy a few sentences previously cited, for they make intelligible these lines of Shelley.

Matter may ultimately be found to be the same in essence, differing only in the arrangement of its particles; or two or three simple substances may produce all the varieties of compound bodies.[1]

Whether matter consists of individual corpuscles, or physical points endowed with attraction and repulsion, still the same conclusions may be formed concerning the powers by which they act, and the quantities in which they combine, and the powers seem capable of being measured by their electrical relations, and the quantities on which they act of being expressed by numbers.[2]

Since all matter may be made to fill a smaller volume by cooling, it is evident that the particles of matter must have space between them; and since every body can communicate the power of expansion to a body of lower temperature, that is, can give an expansive motion to its particles, it is a probable inference that its own particles are possessed of motion; but as there is no change in the position of its parts as long as its temperature is uniform, the motion if it exists, must be a vibratory or undulatory motion, or a motion of the particles round their axes, or a motion of particles round each other.[3]

The "ten thousand orbs involving and involved," the "sphere within sphere," the "thousand sightless axles spinning," "the self-destroying swiftness," the "intense yet self-conflicting speed" can have no other meaning than is explained by the citations from Davy. This is the dance of matter, incessant in motion, a microcosm of involved orbits, yet seem-

[1] Davy, *Elements of Chemical Philosophy*, 181.
[2] *Ibid.*, 57.   [3] *Ibid.*, 95.

ingly at rest. So Davy has conceived it to be and so Shelley, with a scientist's grasp and the imagery of a poet, describes it in terms of color, sound, and movement.[4]

The color and sound and the "unimaginable shapes" push poetic fancy beyond the verge of science, although it may be argued that every element burns with a characteristic color[5] and that, on the analogy of the singing spheres, the minute particles of matter may, in their planetary systems, become vocal likewise. Other suggestions for the sounds of elements lie in the experiments conducted with gases to determine their characteristic pitch. Thus in *Nicholson's Journal* for April, 1799, an article describes apparatus for testing the sounds of various gases. And again in November 1812 is an article "On the Soniferous Vibrations of the Gases." The apparatus described tested gases for pitch and tone and found that each had its characteristic note and quality.

The "unimaginable shapes" which populate the sphere of Shelley's description I take to be reminiscent of Rosicrucian gnomes as in Darwin's mythology. In the strange pseudo-science of Paracelsus the various elements of earth, air, fire,

[4] "Matter, such as we behold it is not inert. It is infinitely active and subtile. Light, electricity and magnetism are fluids not surpassed by thought itself in tenuity and activity: like thought they are sometimes the cause and sometimes the effect of motion; and, distinct as they are from every other class of substances, with which we are acquainted, seem to possess equal claims with thought to the unmeaning distinction of immateriality." *Eusebes and Theosophus (A Refutation of Deism)*, Shelley's Prose Works (Forman), vol. 2, p. 69.

[5] Darwin, again, may have suggested this idea:

> First the fine Forms her dulcet voice requires,
> Which bathe or bask in elemental fires;
> From each bright gem of Day's refulgent car,
> From the pale sphere of every twinkling star,
> From each nice pore of ocean, earth, and air,
> With eye of flame the sparkling hosts repair,
> *Mix their gay hues, in changeful circles play,*
> Like motes, that tenant the meridian ray.
>
> *Botanic Garden*, I. ll. 81-88.

and water are inhabited by "phantasmata," Undines, elemental
spirits of nature, sylphs, pigmies, and salamanders. "Each
species," says Paracelsus, "moves only in the element to which
it belongs, and neither of them can go out of its appropriate
element, which is to them as the air is to us. . . . To each elemental being the element in which it lives is transparent, invisible, and respirable, as the atmosphere is to ourselves."[6]
Again he remarks that "the sun shines through the rocks for
the gnomes." These elementals "are sometimes seen in various shapes." That there were in the universe of Shelley's
imagining creatures of such occult derivation is not improbable in view of his early interest in magic, demons, and
Rosicrucian lore. Certainly it is almost instinctive with Shelley to animate everything, even the seemingly most lifeless
forms of matter. For to one who believes that motion is
evidence of life and mind, and to whom matter itself is but
movement held in balance and seeming rest, the universe to
its minutest part must be an animate thing.

Panthea's further description of the Spirit is full of electrical
lore which is open to a consistent and documented interpretation.

> And from a star upon its forehead shoot,
> Like swords of azure fire or golden spears
> With tyrant-quelling myrtle overtwined,
> Embleming heaven and earth united now,
> Vast beams like spokes of some invisible wheel
> Which whirl as the orb whirls, swifter than thought,
> Filling the abyss with sun-like lightnings,
> And perpendicular now, and now transverse,
> Pierce the dark soil, and as they pierce and pass
> Make bare the secrets of the earth's deep heart; . . .
>
> P. U. IV. ll. 270-279.

[6] Paracelsus, translation by Franz Hartmann, M.D., p. 121. (2 ed., London, 1896).

The star emblematic of the Spirit of the Earth reappears but no longer green as first described. Its rays are "like swords of azure fire or golden spears." This is sufficiently descriptive of the blue electric flame. "Franklin called attention to the resemblance of pale blue flame seen in thundery weather playing about the tips of masts (St. Elmo's fire) and the glow discharge at points."[7] The same expression "azure fire" Shelley had previously employed. One of the shapes seen by Asia within the mist on the journey to the cave of Demogorgon is thus described by Panthea:

> A countenance with beckoning smiles; there burns
> An azure fire within its golden locks.
>
> P. U. II. 3. ll. 51-52.

But in view of the context this explanation may not wholly suffice. That the flame is electric and its corruscations blue and gold is evident, but the "golden spears" of fire are likened to "vast beams like spokes of some invisible wheel" and these "whirl as the orb whirls." The description is suggestive of the phenomenon known as the Aurora Borealis. Passages from the article on the Aurora in Rees's *Cyclopedia* (a work cited by Shelley in the notes to *Queen Mab*) strengthen the likelihood of this identification.

Comparing the appearance of the Southern Lights with the Northern the article points out that whereas the Southern Lights were "always of a whitish color" those of the North "assume various tints especially those of a fiery and purple hue." The article gives the history of the Aurora as recorded in modern times. The first English account is from the year 1560 and the appearance is described as "burning spears." The same term is employed by Cornelius Gemma in describing an illumination in Brabant in 1575. Gemma "compares them to spears, fortified cities, and armies fighting in the air."

[7] Thompson, *Electricity and Magnetism*, 254.

That the phenomenon of the Aurora was electric was long surmised. One evidence in support of the belief was the appearance of an electric discharge in a vacuum. An experimenter "observed, that when the air was most perfectly exhausted, the streams of electric matter were then quite white; but when a small quantity of air was let in the light assumed more of a purple colour. The flashing of this light, therefore, from the dense regions of the atmosphere into such as are more rare, and the transitions through mediums of different densities, he considers as the cause of the aurora borealis, and of the different colours it assumes."[8] That the density of the air, however, has anything to do with the colors of the Aurora the writer of the article does not believe: "For we observe the electric spark sometimes white, sometimes blue, and sometimes purple, in the very same state of the atmosphere, and from the same substance."

The color blue, in any case, is characteristic of the electric spark and sometimes of the Aurora, and the "golden spears" of Shelley are very like the "burning spears" descriptive of the Aurora. What evidence is there that the "vast beams" and the "sun-like lightnings" which fill the abyss are electric? The word "lightnings" in itself is strong presumptive evidence. The theory of the electric currents generated by the earth will afford yet more. Rees's *Cyclopedia* in reviewing the history of scientific speculation upon this theme cites the theory of Halley, god-father of the comet, to the effect that the Aurora "is produced by a kind of subtile matter, or magnetic effluvia, freely pervading the pores of the earth, and which, entering it near its southern pole, passes out again with a like force into the ether at the same distance from the northern. . . . This subtile matter, by becoming some way or other more dense, or having its velocity increased, may be capable

[8] Rees's *Cyclopedia*, article on Aurora Borealis. (1819).

of producing a small degree of light, after the manner of effluvia from electric bodies, which, by a strong and quick friction, emit light in the dark, to which sort of light this seems to have a great affinity."

It is to the speculations of Beccaria, however, that the Cyclopedia accords the last word. Beccaria believed that there was a regular circulation of electric fluid from north to south which he thought to be the cause of magnetism. The Aurora he took to be this stream of electricity made visible by reason of atmospheric conditions. Humphry Davy, it will be recalled, thought that electricity was constantly generated by the internal action of the earth. A citation from Davy will serve better than any other I can find to cap this discussion, approximating very closely, as it does, Shelley's concept and in the phrase "repulsive projectile light" clearly suggesting the "sun-like lightnings."

The electric fluid is probably light in a condensed state; that is, not supplied with the repulsive motion sufficient to give it repulsive projection. Its chemical action upon bodies is similar to that of light; and, when supplied with repulsive motion by friction, or the contact of bodies from which it is capable of subtracting it, it takes the repulsive projectile form, and becomes perceptible as light. It is extremely probable that the great quantity of this fluid almost everywhere diffused on our earth is produced from the condensation of light, from the subtraction of its repulsive motion by black or dark bodies. This fluid, continually formed from the condensation of light, is probably again supplied with repulsive motion at the poles, by the revolution of the earth on its axis, and given off in the form of repulsive projectile light; whilst a quantity equal to that given off by its equilibrating principle is supplied continually from other parts of the globe. Hence the phenomena of the aurora borealis, or northern lights. No more sublime idea can be formed of the motions of matter, than to conceive that the different species are continually changing into each other. The gravitative, the mechanical and the repulsive motions appear to be continually mutually producing each other, and from these changes all the phenomena of the mutation of matter probably arise.[9]

The "sun-like lightnings" generated by the earth and flashing from it "like spokes of some invisible wheel" not only fill the abyss but "pierce the dark soil" and "make bare the secrets of the earth's deep heart." If the expression is taken literally we must suppose that Shelley conceived of some radiant energy such as the X-ray of later discovery capable of penetrating matter. He would have perceived its theoretical possibility but I know of no scientific hypothesis of his time which could have suggested the idea to him.[9a] I think it more likely that he is speaking figuratively of electric powers. It will be recalled that it was through electro-chemical processes of analysis that Humphry Davy discovered several new elements. In his Bakerian lecture of Nov. 19, 1807 he had announced the discovery by a new electro-chemical analytical process of the elements potassium and sodium. On June 30, 1808 he announced the discovery of barium, strontium, calcium, and magnium through the decomposition of the earths. Thus he pierced the "dark soil" and laid earth's secrets bare.

The passage lends itself to an interpretation in terms of electric phenomena known to Shelley. I can conceive of no other which will render it intelligible. If the interpretation given is not granted, the lines are merely fanciful description and Shelley is no more than a "pretty poet." No one who has persevered thus far in this analysis will, I take it, think Shelley to be that. He may push metaphor to the verge of human understanding but it becomes clear as one labors in his wake

[9] *Memoirs of the Life of Sir H. Davy*, I, 46.

[9a] It may be noted, however, that were the latent electricity of Davy's hypothesis to become perceptible as light in its exit from the earth's interior, it would necessarily act much like the X-ray and reveal the matter through which it passed.

that an intellectual concept underlies his most subtle fancies. And so, I believe, there is some hidden implication in the phrase "tyrant-quelling myrtle" innocent as it appears. Why are the "golden spears" overtwined with myrtle and how does the myrtle symbolize the union of heaven and earth?

Myrtle is sacred to Venus, and its leaves, like those of the laurel, were employed in Roman times to crown victors in an ovation. Plutarch is authority for the statement that a general was crowned with myrtle when he had won a bloodless victory through diplomacy rather than arms. Its associations are therefore pacific and appropriate to the goddess of love. Laurel also was used to crown victors, however, and laurel is peculiarly associated with lightning. Pliny says of it: "Another reason, too, may be the fact, that of all the shrubs that are planted and received in our houses, this is the only one that is never struck by lightning."[10] And he states that the Emperor Tiberius "was in the habit of putting on a wreath of laurel to allay his apprehensions of disastrous effects from the lightning."[11] Again Pliny observes that "among the productions of the earth, thunder never strikes the laurel."[12]

Altogether laurel has a much more distinguished history than the myrtle. It is associated with emperors over whose gates it was hung both "because it was looked upon as a protection against lightning and because it was considered an emblem of immortality."[13] The laurel is also an antidote to the venom of the seps and the dipsas, serpents mentioned by Shelley in *Prometheus* on the authority of Lucan and Pliny. It is a plausible surmise that, by reason of the use of both in crowning victors, Shelley confused the traditions of the laurel and the myrtle and ascribed to the latter the protective virtues of the former. A further citation from Beccaria lends color to

[10] *Pliny*, XV, Chap. 40.
[11] *Ibid.*
[12] *Ibid.*, II, 56.
[13] *Ibid.*, XV, 35.

this guess. Beccaria writes that a "Mr. Maimbray in Edinburgh, electrified two myrtles, during the whole month of October, in the year 1746, and observed, that they vegetated more quickly than other myrtles not electrified."[14] With this detail freshly in mind it would be easy for Shelley to employ the myrtle where the more appropriate symbol would be the laurel.

Let me turn now to one of the most fascinating and baffling passages in the poem, Ione's description of the orb-like chariot symbolical of the moon, a passage which precedes that of the sphere in which the infant Spirit of the Earth lies asleep.

> I see a chariot like that thinnest boat
> In which the Mother of the Months is borne
> By ebbing light into her western cave,
> When she upsprings from interlunar dreams;
> O'er which is curved an orblike canopy
> Of gentle darkness, and the hills and woods,
> Distinctly seen through that dusk aery veil,
> Regard like shapes in an enchanter's glass;
> Its wheels are solid clouds, azure and gold,
> Such as the genii of the thunderstorm
> Pile on the floor of the illumined sea
> When the sun rushes under it; they roll
> And move and grow as with an inward wind;
> Within it sits a wingèd infant, white
> Its countenance, like the whiteness of bright snow,
> Its plumes are as feathers of sunny frost,
> Its limbs gleam white, through the wind-flowing folds
> Of its white robe, woof of ethereal pearl.
> Its hair is white, the brightness of white light
> Scattered in strings; yet its two eyes are heavens
> Of liquid darkness, which the Deity
> Within seems pouring, as a storm is poured
> From jaggèd clouds, out of their arrowy lashes,
> Tempering the cold and radiant air around,

---

[14] Beccaria, *Artificial Electricity*, 279.

With fire that is not brightness; in its hand
It sways a quivering moonbeam, from whose point
A guiding power directs the chariot's prow
Over its wheelèd clouds, which as they roll
Over the grass, and flowers, and waves, make sounds,
Sweet as a singing rain of silver dew.

                                        P. U. IV. ll. 206-235.

Inasmuch as the description which follows, of the translucent orb in which the Spirit of the Earth lies asleep, was
found to be emblematical of the physical properties of the
earth, it is reasonable to suppose that the long passage descriptive of the wingèd infant in the orb-like chariot is, analo-
gously, descriptive of the physical properties of the moon. The
difficulty lies in determining what of the lines are merely
visual and what are expressive of scientific facts. Thus the
"orb-like canopy of gentle darkness" and the "hills and woods
distinctly seen through that dusk aery veil" I take to be a
poetic and purely visual depiction of the new moon in whose
arms, in clear weather, the old moon is "distinctly seen" but
"through a dusk aery veil." The orb-like canopy of the chariot
is translucent, and through its "gentle darkness" hills and
woods are distinct but faintly remote and unreal. This is
visually precise and is, in a sense, emblematical, but, I take it,
of physical properties which are a matter of common visual
knowledge.

I shall, therefore, stress those lines which seem to me to
have a hidden scientific significance, perfectly aware that I
may have overlooked implications of importance in other lines.
For me the fascination of the passage lies in the reiterated
emphasis on whiteness and coldness, the "sunny frost;" the
curious description of the hair, with the expression "the
brightness of white light scattered in strings;" and the "liquid
darkness" which tempers the "cold and radiant air around,

with fire that is not brightness." In these lines I think is implicit Shelley's chief knowledge of the physical peculiarities of the moon.

The whiteness and coldness are simple enough. Erasmus Darwin, it will be recalled, emphasizes these qualities.

> Dimpled with vales, with shining hills emboss'd,
> And roll'd round Earth her airless realms of frost.
> *Botanic Garden,* II. ll. 81-2.

In a note upon these lines Darwin commented upon the lack of atmosphere in the moon and its coldness. But he remarked also that as the moon seems still "to suffer much by volcanoes, a sufficient quantity of air may in process of time be generated to produce an atmosphere; which may prevent its heat from so easily escaping, and its water from so easily evaporating."

At the present time then, according to Darwin, the moon develops heat which radiates because there is no atmosphere to retain it, and the surface of the moon remains congealed. But why the emphasized whiteness? This, I take it, is explained by the lack of atmosphere of the moon, for the sunlight is reflected back unbroken. There is no prism of air to refract the light and to produce color. A number of passages in *Prometheus,* as well as a passage in *Queen Mab,* reveal Shelley's interest in this phenomenon. In the invocation of Prometheus early in the poem occur the lines

> Thou serenest Air,
> Through which the Sun walks burning without beams!
> *P. U.* I. ll. 64-5.

The allusion is to the upper tenuous atmosphere in which the sun's rays, in Shelley's belief, would be conveyed without being visible. Again the allusion to the necessity of an atmosphere to the refraction of light and the creation of color is evident in the lines spoken by the Voice from the Air

I had clothed, since Earth uprose,
Its wastes in colors not their own.
P. U. I. ll. 82-3.

And again in the Song of the Spirits describing the descent to
the cave of Demogorgon

Through the gray, void abysm,
Down, down!
Where the air is no prism,
P. U. I. ll. 72-4.

That color resides not in the object but in its ability to
absorb and to reflect certain of the air-refracted rays of light
was, it may be recalled, one of the discoveries of Newton.
Perhaps it will not be amiss to quote again briefly a few sentences expressive of the idea, for it is clear that it is a fact
which made a great impression on Shelley: "If the sun's light
consisted of but one sort of rays, there would be but one colour
in the whole world. . . ."[15] "All the productions and appearances of colours in the world are derived not from any physical
change caused in light by refraction or reflection, but only
from the various mixtures or separation of rays, by virtue of
their different refrangibility or reflexibility."[16]   To this may
be added Shelley's own note upon lines 242-3, part I, of *Queen
Mab:*

The sun's unclouded orb
Rolled through the black concave.

Beyond our atmosphere the sun would appear a rayless orb of fire
in the midst of a black concave. The equal diffusion of its light
on earth is owing to the refraction of the rays by the atmosphere
and their reflection from other bodies.

There is sufficient evidence here to explain the emphasis
upon the whiteness of the moon and possibly to explain the

[15] Newton, *Opticks,* I, 2, p. 90 (1704).
[16] *Ibid.,* II, 2, p. 48.

likeness of the moon's hair—presumably its radiant light—to the "brightness of white light scattered in strings." For if the moon has no atmosphere there will be no bending of the light rays, which will be reflected directly without curvature. That Shelley was aware of the curving of the light rays in the atmosphere is evident from a line in *The Cloud*.

> And the winds and sunbeams with their
> convex gleams
>
> l. 79.

For "in general, the course of a ray passing through the atmosphere, is that of a curve, which is concave toward the earth."[17] If concave towards the earth it would be to the cloud, lying above the earth, convex.

I am not satisfied that the explanation thus far wholly elucidates the expression "scattered in strings," which surely suggests some phenomenon of light that is not a reasoned conclusion but a visual memory born of a laboratory experience. I shall revert to the expression shortly when I advance an alternative explanation for the passage. The "liquid darkness" meanwhile demands attention.

As an explanation for this I am satisfied with what has been advanced in the earlier chapters upon Herschel and Davy anent the black rays of Herschel's discovery. Shelley employs the phenomenon to image forth the formless might of Demogorgon:

> I see a mighty darkness
> Filling the seat of power, and rays of gloom
> Dart round, as light from the meridian sun.
>
> *P. U.* II. 4. ll. 3-5.

Demogorgon, like the "deep truth," is depicted as imageless but radiating power, and Shelley's figure clearly derives from Herschel's discovery. That energy from the moon absorbed

---

[17] *Nicholson's Journal*, July 1799, p. 141.

from the sun can thus emanate in black rays was a speculation advanced by Davy as previously quoted.[18]   Also there is Herschel's supposed discovery of volcanic action in the moon and the production of heat which, if not retained by the moon, because of its lack of atmosphere, must radiate in this fashion. Hence the "liquid darkness" that tempers the "cold and radiant air around with fire that is not brightness." The explanation is consistent but for the word "air" and this may be explained if we conceive the moon to possess a very tenuous atmosphere, one that permits the phenomenon to function as described. Indeed Darwin's note upon the moon, from which an excerpt was previously made, employs the expression "that the moon possesses little or no atmosphere."

That the explanations thus far advanced do not, however, explain fully the "white light scattered in strings" leads to another speculation not indeed out of harmony with that already advanced but complementary to it. Throughout the poem Shelley conceives the earth and moon as masculine and feminine, the moon as the earth's bride and held to her spouse by the forces of gravitation and magnetism. In view of our history of the speculations which assumed these forces to be the same as electrical attraction, it imposes no strain upon Shelley's conception to consider earth and moon as the two poles of an electric circuit, this all the more in that the star upon the forehead of the earth seems to identify it with the negative electrode of a battery.

The terms "star" and "brush" to denote the appearance of the light upon the two electrodes are employed by Beccaria and seem to have passed into general use (See Rees's *Cyclopedia*.) The use of the word "star" was previously defined in Beccaria's terms. The "brush," his term for the electric fire emanating from an electrode, as "star" is employed to charac-

[18] See p. 111.

terize the fire at the point at which it enters, is thus described
by him:

> The brush has the appearance of a little conical *fascis* of rays,
> two thirds of an inch, or an inch, or even more in length . . . the
> fire subdivides itself into rays which grow continually more numer-
> ous, and proportionably thinner, as also more languid.[19]

The term "pencil of rays" (Rees's *Cyclopedia*) is also employed as descriptive of this brush. In all descriptions the
notable point is the clear divergence and separateness of the
rays as distinguished from the appearance of the "star."

There is, however, a further possibility to consider. A good
deal of experimentation is recorded relative to the passage of
an electric current through various gases and through a
vacuum. In view of the moon's attenuated atmosphere the
passage from moon to earth of an electrical current would
presumably be accompanied, in the sphere of the moon's thin
atmosphere, by the light effects observable in passing an
electric charge through a tube in which the air had been
nearly exhausted.

It is not unlikely that Shelley was depicting in the "white
light scattered in strings" the counterpart on the moon of the
aurora borealis on the earth. I cited a passage attributing the
colors of the northern aurora to the different densities of the
atmosphere. In a very attenuated atmosphere, as presumably
on the moon, its color would be white. The southern aurora
as observed by Captain Cook "consisted of long columns of
a clear white light shooting up from the horizon to the
zenith."[20] Whether this whiteness was due to its manifestation in a rarer atmosphere than in the north, or whether, as
might be thought, a white emanation was characteristic of one
pole and a colored emanation of the other, does not clearly

[19] Beccaria, *Artificial Electricity*, 38.
[20] Rees's *Cyclopedia*, article on Aurora Borealis.

appear, but either explanation may be made to fit Shelley's description. If the earth is one pole of an electric circuit and is characterized by a star of colored light, the moon the other pole, characterized by the brush, may appropriately be white. The correspondence then lies between earth and moon as between the northern and southern magnetic poles and their elctrical effects, the one colored, the other white.

If, however, Shelley in characterizing the electric emanation of the moon has no such elaborate duality in mind and intends to symbolize only the character of an electric discharge in an attenuated medium, there is a wealth of experiment to explain his use of the white light in strings. I shall content myself with presenting two experiments as described by Priestley, for these are such as Shelley might easily have himself performed. In one a spark is passed through a receiver exhausted of air (undoubtedly not a complete vacuum, however). The spark becomes visible "through the whole length of the vacuum" as "a broad stream of light. . . . This stream often divides itself into a variety of beautiful rivulets, which are continually changing their course, uniting and dividing again in a most pleasing manner."[21]

The second experiment is thus described:

But the most beautiful of all the experiments that can be exhibited by the electric light is Mr. Canton's *Aurora Borealis,* of which the following is but an imperfect description. Make a Torricellian vacuum in a glass tube, about three feet long, and seal it hermetically, whereby it will always be ready for use. Let one end of this tube be held in the hand, and the other applied to the conductor, and immediately the whole tube will be illuminated, from end to end; and when taken from the conductor, will continue luminous without interruption for a considerable time, very often above a quarter of an hour. . . .[22]

[21] Joseph Priestley, *The History and Present State of Electricity with Original Experiments,* 524. (1775).
[22] *Ibid.,* 525.

What emerges from this all too extensive citation? No certainty, I believe, as to Shelley's precise intent, for all of the possibilities suggested are plausible. Yet the solutions have elements in common; all are consonant with the effects of light in a very rare atmosphere, light that is white, unrefracted, emanating in rays rather than as a diffused and luminous effect. That Shelley was thinking of an electric discharge seems to me likely in view of his description of the aurora in his analogous depiction of the earth. But whether he considers the earth and moon as the two electrodes of a circuit is not certain. He may, in describing the moon, be thinking only of the effect in the moon of a discharge similar to the aurora in our denser terrestrial atmosphere. That the "liquid darkness," however, refers to the "dark rays" seems to me unmistakable.

In the latter part of this study I lay myself open, I well realize, to the charge of making a case, of pushing the implications beyond the verge of probability. I would have the reader pause and reflect, therefore, that some of the most incredible interpretations were most fully documented and proved. That proof was established of the atmospheric electricity so wholly based on Beccaria. In the difficult moon passage there seem to me to be several possible interpretations, yet all with common elements and reconcilable. No one of the interpretations is as subtle and difficult as was Shelley's identification of atmospheric electricity with the Spirit of the Earth. But in the moon passage Shelley has not left so single and certain a clue as in the other or, if he has, I have failed to detect it.

CHAPTER X

PROMETHEUS UNBOUND: ASTRONOMICAL ALLUSIONS

Demogorgon addressing the Earth:

> Thou, Earth, calm empire of a happy soul,
> Sphere of divinest shapes and harmonies,
> Beautiful orb! gathering as thou dost roll
> The love which paves thy path along the skies.
>
> *P. U.* IV. ll. 519-522.

The earth in Shelley's mythology is an animate spirit. The "love" which it generates as it rolls is, in one sense, electrical energy, as has been sufficiently demonstrated. But what is the cosmogony of which the earth is a part? The earth's relation to the moon will serve as a partial answer to the question.

A lover-like relationship between the Spirits of the Earth and Moon is early predicted. Asia speaks to the Spirit of the Earth:

> And never will we part, till thy chaste sister,
> Who guides the frozen and inconstant moon,
> Will look on thy more warm and equal light
> Till her heart thaw like flakes of April snow
> And love thee.
>
> *Spirit of the Earth*
> What! as Asia loves Prometheus?
>
> *Asia*
> Peace, wanton! thou art yet not old enough
> Think ye by gazing on each other's eyes
> To multiply your lovely selves, and fill
> With spherèd fires the interlunar air?
>
> *P. U.* III. 4. ll. 86-94.

The "spherèd fires" which fill the "interlunar air" may be no more than a figure of speech expressive of fruitful love, but it is likely that more is meant, for Shelley in these matters usually contrives to make his figures expressive both of an emotional and a physical fact or, better, to endow a physical fact with an emotional significance. I shall have more to say in another connection of "falling stones" and meteorites and the theory of their origin. It suffices here to note that an opinion widely held ascribes their origin to the moon:

> Lastly, some with the illustrious author of the Mecanique Celeste, are of opinion, they are bodies projected from the moon, which notion has been adopted by the greatest part of English philosophers.[1]

In the fourth act of *Prometheus* we have depicted the new Promethean age. The moon is now the bride of the earth and beneath the influence of the earth's "love"—for which, physically, read electricity, magnetism, gravity, and heat—is blossoming into new life.

> The Moon (To The Earth).
> All suns and constellations shower
> On thee a light, a life, a power,
> Which doth array thy sphere; thou pourest thine
> On mine, on mine!
>
> *P. U.* IV. ll. 440-443.

The light, life, and power poured by all the suns and constellations upon the earth and in turn by the earth upon the moon is to be simply interpreted in Newtonian terms. Newton had demonstrated that the celestial bodies exert an influence each one upon all the others. This gravitational pull, it will be recalled, was to be thought of as magnetic or electrical, for Newton employs the terms as virtually synonymous. And light, also, was shown to be but one expression of the all-pervasive electrical ether.

[1] Marcel de Serres in *Nicholson's Journal*, XXXV, 242. (1813).

The Promethean day seems to premise a fresh liberation
of energy born of love, and this energy, emanating from the
earth, transforms the moon. Greater heat permits the development on the moon of an atmosphere in which clouds may
soar. With clouds, rain and the fertility of the moon come
into being. Living shapes appear. Apparently, in Shelley's
philosophy, much of the force of the world, as expressed in
Jove's thunder-bolts, had been turned to malignant purposes;
was indeed hate, not love. This force, in the reign of Prometheus, is liberated for loving and beneficent ends. Earth and
moon, therefore, feel warmth and life.

> Gazing on thee I feel, I know
> Green stalks burst forth, and bright flowers grow,
> And living shapes upon my bosom move;
> Music is in the sea and air,
> Wingèd clouds soar here and there
> Dark with the rain new buds are dreaming of:
> 'Tis love, all love!
>> *P. U.* IV. ll. 363-369.

And again:

> The snow upon my lifeless mountains
> Is loosened into living fountains,
> My solid oceans flow, and sing and shine:
>> *P. U.* IV. ll. 356-358.

Erasmus Darwin's note will be recalled:

That the moon possesses little or no atmosphere is deduced
from the undiminished lustre of the stars at the instant when
they emerge behind her disk. That the ocean of the moon is
frozen, is confirmed from there being no appearance of lunar
tides. . . .[2]

From a long lyric full of astronomical implications I cite
what seem to me the significant lines:

[2] *Botanic Garden*, note to l. 82, Canto II.

Thou art speeding round the sun
Brightest world of many a one:

. . . .

I, thy crystal paramour,
Borne beside thee by a power
Like the polar Paradise,
Magnet-like, of lovers' eyes;
I, a most enamoured maiden
Whose weak brain is overladen
With the pleasure of her love,
Maniac-like around thee move,
Gazing, an insatiate bride,
On thy form from every side,

. . . .

Brother, *wheresoe'er thou soarest*
I must hurry, whirl and follow
Through the heavens wide and hollow,
Sheltered by the warm embrace
Of thy soul from hungry space,
Drinking from thy sense and sight
Beauty, majesty and might,

P. U. IV. ll. 457-482.

Gravitational force is symbolized in the "warm embrace."
"Maniac-like around thee move" is intelligible in the light of
the obvious movements of the moon. But more may be implied in the "maniac-like" than this.

The Earth and the Moon also mutually attract each other; but
the irregularities in the Moon's motion proceed principally from
the attraction of the sun. . . .[3]

[3] Buffon, *Natural History*, "On the Formation of Planets," 25. The passage
has a double significance as linking Shelley's science with his Platonism. The
observation has been previously made by Miss Winstanley in her excellent
essay *Platonism in Shelley.*
"In the fourth act of *Prometheus Unbound,* Shelley in the most magical
way, blends his Platonism with the ideas of modern astronomy. In the
Timaeus the law of gravitation is explained by Plato as being not only an
attraction of lesser bodies to greater, but as having a magnetic power. Shelley
avails himself of this idea: the Moon and the Earth he represents as living

The irregularity of the moon's orbit is remarked by all astronomers and Shelley must have been acquainted with it.
Possibly one further citation will not seem redundant:

But that orbit [the moon's] is subject to considerable variations;
with respect to figure, eccentricity, etc. which are incomparably
greater than the variations of the orbits of the earth, or of the
other primary planets. This arises from the action of the sun upon
the moon, which sometimes conspires with, and at other times is
contrary to, the earth's action upon the same. Yet those apparent
irregularities are all conformable to, and depending upon, the
grand law of universal attraction or gravitation.[4]

More interesting are the lines

> Borne beside thee by a power
> Like the polar Paradise,
> Magnet-like, of lovers' eyes.

Just how these are grammatically to be construed is not
clear to me. Is this the sense: "a power like" (that of) "the
polar Paradise" which is magnet-like and resident in lover's
eyes? The moon, at any rate, is bound to the earth by a
magnetic attraction which is akin to love in the eyes of lovers.
Hence the expression "polar Paradise," the eyes of the lovers
being likened to the poles of a magnetic circuit. It isn't
wholly a satisfactory simile as phrased. The magnetic implications, however, are evident and I shall cite again a passage
from Gilbert as evidence that a magnetic relation of earth to
moon had long been believed to exist.

The force which emanates from the moon reaches to the earth,
and, in like manner, the magnetic virtue of the earth pervades the
region of the moon . . . the earth attracts and repels the moon,

spirits, and the force of gravity which binds them together as the magnetic
attraction of their love." L. Winstanley in *Essays and Studies by Members of
the English Association*, Vol. IV. (Oxford, 1913).

[4] Tiberius Cavallo, *Elements of Natural and Experimental Philosophy*, IV,
111. (1803).

and the moon, within certain limits, the earth; not so as to make the bodies come together, as magnetic bodies do, but so that they may go on in a continuous course.[5]

There is still a further connotation in the phrase "polar Paradise" which should be mentioned. In one of his Notes to *Queen Mab,* Shelley, it will be remembered, spoke of the evidences in fossil remains of tropical life once existent in what are now the arctic regions.[6] Darwin's picture of the evolving earth had described such a phase of its early history, one in which there was a uniformly equable climate and in which the later cataclysms of nature were unknown. This was the legendary golden age which, with the liberation of Prometheus and the return to beneficent purposes of energy diverted by Jupiter for his tyrannical ends, is to be renewed. Thus the "polar Paradise" may have its literal physical meaning as well as its symbolical meaning.

The lines

> Sheltered by the warm embrace
> Of thy soul from hungry space

mean, obviously, that the gravitational pull of the earth keeps the moon from flying off into space. Documentation is superfluous. The thought is identical with that expressed in another passage:

> As the sun rules even with a tyrant's gaze
>   The unquiet republic of the maze
> Of planets, struggling fierce towards heaven's free wilderness.
>
> *P. U.* IV. ll. 397-399.

Shelley's astronomy is basically Newtonian with the addition of the nebular hypothesis of Laplace and the observations

[5] From Gilbert's *De Mundo Nostro Sublunari Philosophia Nova* (1631). Cited by A. J. Snow, *Matter and Gravity in Newton's Physical Philosophy,* 140. (Oxford University Press, 1926).

[6] See p. 25.

of Herschel. I noted in the chapter on Herschel that in June 1818 Herschel formally renounced his earlier belief that the stellar universe was finite and doomed therefore to extinction through the force of gravitation pulling all matter to one dead center. It is evident from the lyrics of the fourth act of *Prometheus* that Shelley clung to Herschel's earlier theory, and in all likelihood had never learned of Herschel's retraction.

> Our spoil is won
> Our task is done,
> We are free to dive, or soar, or run;
> Beyond and around,
> Or within the bound
> Which clips the world with darkness round.
>
> We'll pass the eyes
> Of the starry skies
> Into the hoar deep to colonize;
> Death, Chaos and Night,
> From the sound of our flight,
> Shall flee, like mist from a tempest's might.
>
> And Earth, Air and Light
> And the Spirit of Might,
> Which drives round the stars in their fiery flight;
> And Love, Thought and Breath,
> The powers that quell Death,
> Wherever we soar shall assemble beneath.
>
> And our singing shall build
> In the void's loose field
> A world for the Spirit of Wisdom to wield;
> We will take our plan
> From the new world of man,
> And our work shall be called the Promethean.
>
> *P. U.* IV. ll. 135-158.

The expression "the bound which clips the world with darkness round" must allude to Herschel's earlier belief in a finite universe. The expressions the "hoar deep" and the "void's loose field" must refer to the nebulous stuff fringing the stellar universe. From this nebulous matter, verifying the nebular hypothesis, Herschel traced numerous groups of stars and solar systems in various degrees of evolution. The process in its later phase is depicted in another passage from *Prometheus*. The semi-chorus of liberated spirits now devoting their energies to new acts of creation sing thus:

> We whirl, singing loud, round the gathering sphere,
> Till the trees, and the beasts, and the clouds appear
> From its chaos made calm by love, not fear;
>
> *P. U.* IV. ll. 169-171.

The "heaven's free wilderness" of a previous quotation must likewise refer to the chaos or "void's loose field" of nebulous stuff outside the ordered and evolved stellar universe.

The activities of the liberated spirits in the fourth act are expressive of two kinds of motion, the centrifugal:

> We, beyond heaven, are driven along
>
> *P. U.* IV. l. 161.

and

> Ceaseless, and rapid, and fierce, and free,
> With the Spirits which build a new earth and sea,
> And a heaven where yet heaven could never be.
>
> *P. U.* IV. ll. 163-5.

The centripetal forces "the enchantments of earth retain":

> Solemn, and slow, and serene, and bright,
> Leading the Day, and outspeeding the Night,
> With the powers of a world of perfect light;
>
> *P. U.* IV. ll. 166-168.

And the spirits personifying both kinds of forces sing:

Wherever we fly we lead along
In leashes, like star-beams, soft yet strong,
The clouds that are heavy with love's sweet rain.
                    P. U. IV. ll. 177-179.

The clouds and the rain are the symbols of fertility and life
and these are led by the forces of electric attraction whose
spiritual counterpart is love.

An allusion in another passage I take to be of a more
speculative sort, wholly without the field of Herschel's astronomy:

Ye kings of suns and stars, Daemons and Gods,
    Ethereal Dominations, who possess
Elysian, windless, fortunate abodes
Beyond Heaven's constellated wilderness:
                    P. U. IV. ll. 529-532.

The passage is an interesting one, with philosophical and
mystical implications which may suffice to explain it. Yet the
citation from Newton which follows endows the lines with a
certain reality which they otherwise lack.

It is possible, that in the remote regions of the fixed stars, or
perhaps far beyond them, there may be some body absolutely at
rest; but impossible to know, from the position of bodies to one
another in our regions, whether any of these do keep the same
position to that remote body; it follows that absolute rest cannot
be determined from the position of bodies in our regions.[7]

Mr. A. N. Whitehead has pointed out a notable instance
of Shelley's power of visualizing an astronomical relation:

The Earth speaks:
I spin beneath my pyramid of night
Which points into the heavens,—dreaming delight
Murmuring victorious joy in my enchanted sleep:

[7] Newton, *Principles,* I, 9. Cited by Burtt, *Metaphysical Foundations of
Physics,* 247.

As a youth lulled in love-dreams faintly sighing,
Under the shadow of his beauty lying
Which round his rest a watch of light and warmth doth keep.

P. U. IV. ll. 444-449.

"This stanza," Mr. Whitehead observes, "could only have been written by someone with a definite geometrical diagram before his inward eye—a diagram which it has often been my business to demonstrate to mathematical classes. As evidence, note especially the last line, which gives poetical imagery to the light surrounding night's pyramid. The idea could not occur to anyone without the diagram. But the whole poem and other poems are permeated with touches of this kind."[8]

What is odd in this citation is Shelley's use of the word "pyramid" for the phenomenon more accurately described by the word "cone."

The moon, the earth, and the other planets, being opaque bodies, must necessarily cast a shadow on the side opposite to the sun's; and as every one of the planets is smaller than the sun, that shadow must evidently be conical.[9]

I believe that Shelley's use of "pyramid" in this instance is reminiscent of Pliny's use of the word in the same connection.

. . . For night is nothing more than the shade of the earth. The figure of this shade is like that of a pyramid or an inverted top; and the moon enters it only near its point and it does not exceed the height of the moon, for there is no other star which is obscured in the same manner, while a figure of this kind always terminates in a point.[10]

And again:

For there are shadows of three figures. . . . If the body be less than the light, then we shall have the figure of a pyramid, terminating in a point.[11]

[8] *Science and the Modern World*, 163.
[9] Tiberius Cavallo, *Elements of Natural and Experimental Philosophy*, IV, 125.
[10] Pliny, *Natural History*, Book II, cap. 7, p. 34.
[11] *Ibid.*, 36.

Herschel's exploration of the heavens had disclosed the vast number of the celestial bodies and from his observation of the stages of their evolution he had concluded that many of them were, like our earth, habitable. He speaks of them as "habitable planetary globes." Both the number and the suitability of the stars to human life are brought out in Shelley's lines:

> Then, see those million worlds which burn and roll
> Around us: their inhabitants beheld
> My spherèd light wane in wide heaven;
>
> *P. U.* I. ll. 163-5.

Other allusions, wholly or in part astronomical, will be cited in various connections. This chapter I shall conclude with a passage which is slightly ambiguous:

> He taught the implicated orbits woven
> Of the wide-wandering stars; and how the sun
> Changes his lair, and by what secret spell
> The pale moon is transformed, when her broad eye
> Gazes not on the interlunar sea.
>
> *P. U.* II. 4. ll. 87-91.

Professor John M. Manly suggests that by "implicated orbits" is meant 'other than concentric,' and that the "wide wandering stars" are therefore comets. The word "implicated" is used in *Alastor*.

> The meeting boughs and implicated leaves.
>
> *Alastor*, l. 426.

The meaning here is, plainly, 'involved' or 'interwoven.' "Implicated orbits" could mean those of comets or, conceivably, those of the planets of our solar system. The early knowledge of astronomy described in the passage would seem not to imply a fact so recondite as the return of comets in predictable orbits were it not that one of Shelley's known authorities, mentioned in the notes to *Queen Mab,* was M. Bailly, the noted French astronomer. In his *Letters to Voltaire*[12] Bailly sets forth his thesis that the Chaldeans, Chinese, and Indians are all descendants of a people which once inhabited the northern and central parts of Asia, a people of a high degree of culture whose knowledge of astronomy was profound. The astronomical lore of the Chaldeans was, Bailly believes, only the vestiges of this ancient wisdom, for among the Chaldeans "le retour des cometes ètait une opinion plutôt qu' un principe."[13] So extraordinary a belief, one which was reestablished as a principle only in the seventeenth century, argues the preexistence of a culture very old and advanced, Bailly believes. The emphasis which he gives this curious fact, together with his ascription of this ancient culture to an age which has lingered in tradition as the "golden age," makes Bailly a plausible source for Shelley's description of the days when Prometheus fostered the arts and sciences among men. The "wide wandering stars" may tentatively, then, be identified as comets.

For the expression "how the sun changes his lair" the interpretation need not be so recondite. All that is meant, I think, is the observations of the ancient astronomers as to the seeming movement of the sun in relation to the constellations. If the sun's actual movement is meant, Shelley alludes to the discovery made by Herschel that our solar system is moving towards the constellation Hercules.

[12] *Lettres sur L'Origine des Sciences, et sur celle des Peuples de L'Asie. Addressées à M. de Voltaire par M. Bailly* (1777).
[13] *Bailly,* 46.

CHAPTER XI

PROMETHEUS UNBOUND: OTHER SCIENTIFIC ALLUSIONS

IT WAS by reason of the similarity of a passage in the *Botanic Garden* to one in *Prometheus* that the identification of atmospheric electricity with the Spirit of the Earth could be established. Darwin's science is but half transformed to poetry. Moreover Darwin supplies notes. Shelley so assimilates his science to his poetical method that the scientific implication would often be wholly unguessed were there not some lucky clue to its meaning in Darwin or elsewhere. The following passages illustrate this truth admirably. I shall cite first the lines from the *Botanic Garden* and discuss Darwin's annotations of them. Then I shall quote the parallel passage from *Prometheus* and follow it with further scientific excerpts.

Darwin has been evoking the Ethereal Powers who

> Chase the shooting stars
> Or yoke the vollied lightnings to your cars
> *Botanic Garden*, I. ll. 115-16.

a line which recalls Shelley's similar concept in

> My coursers are fed with the lightning.

Darwin then goes on to recount various of the activities of these "ethereal powers."

> Or, plum'd with flame, in gay battalion's spring
> To brighter regions borne on broader wing
> Where lighter gases, circumfused on high,
> Form the vast concave of exterior sky.
> Ride, with broad eye and scintillating hair,
> The rapid Fire-ball through the midnight air;
> Dart from the North on pale electric streams,

Fringing Night's sable robe with transient beams.
Or rein the Planets in their swift careers,
Gilding with borrow'd light their twinkling spheres;
Alarm with comet-blaze the sapphire plain,
The wan stars glimmering through its silver train;

Botanic Garden, I. ll. 127-134.

Darwin's notes explain that by the "lighter gases" hydrogen is meant, which is "perpetually rising" from the decomposition of animals and vegetables. This hydrogen, rising above the aerial atmosphere, forms a super atmosphere. "Between the termination of the aerial and the beginning of the gaseous atmosphere, the airs will occasionally be intermixed, and thus become inflammable by the electric spark; these circumstances will assist in explaining the phenomena of fire balls, northern lights, and of some variable winds, and long-continued rains."

The passage in *Prometheus* which more poetically expresses similar ideas is the dialogue of the fauns in the second act.

First Faun

Canst thou imagine where those spirits live
Which make such delicate music in the woods?
We haunt within the least frequented caves
And closest coverts, and we know these wilds,
Yet never meet them, though we hear them oft:
Where may they hide themselves?

Second Faun

'Tis hard to tell;
I have heard those more skilled in spirits say,
The bubbles, which the enchantment of the sun
Sucks from the pale faint water-flowers that pave
The oozy bottom of clear lakes and pools,
Are the pavilions where such dwell and float
Under the green and golden atmosphere
Which noontide kindles through the woven leaves;

And when these burst, and the thin fiery air,
The which they breathed within those lucent domes,
Ascends to flow like meteors through the night,
They ride on them, and rein their headlong speed,
And bow their burning crests, and glide in fire
Under the waters of the earth again.

First Faun

If such live thus, have others other lives,
Under pink blossoms or within the bells
Of meadow flowers or folded violets deep,
Or on their dying odors, when they die,
Or in the sunlight of the spherèd dew?

                              P. U. II. 2. ll. 64-87.

The bubbles are the hydrogen gas which the action of the
sun liberates from the vegetation at the bottom of lakes and
pools. This liberated gas, as in Darwin's description, is electrically ignited and flows in the form of a meteor back to the
waters of the earth. Exactly the same phenomenon is described in the two passages and there are echoes in Shelley of
Darwin's imagery. In Darwin, the spirits "ride . . . . the
rapid fire-ball." In Shelley, the spirits ride the meteors. In
Darwin occurs the phrase "with broad eye and scintillating
hair." In Shelley, "and bow their burning crests." Shelley
in the lines which follow carries the scientific conception farther, however, than does Darwin. There are "others" which
"have other lives," that is, other activities of the gas or gases.
The whole passage is completely explained by the following
quotations from Erasmus Darwin's Additional Notes.

(a) The air is perpetually subject to increase or diminution
from its combination with other bodies, or its evolution from them.
The vital part of the air, called oxygen, is continually produced in
this climate from the perspiration of vegetables in the sunshine,
and probably from the action of light on clouds or on water in
the tropical climates, where the sun has greatest power, and may

exert some yet unknown laws of luminous combination. Another part of the atmosphere, which is called azote [nitrogen], is perpetually set at liberty from animal and vegetable bodies by putrefaction or combustion, from many springs of water, from volatile alcali, and probably from fixed alcali, of which there is an exhaustless source in the water of the ocean. Both these component parts of the air are perpetually again diminished by their contact with the soil, which covers the surface of the earth, producing nitre. The oxygene is diminished in the production of all acids, of which the carbonic and muriatic exist in great abundance. The azote is diminished in the growth of animal bodies, of which it constitutes an important part, or in its combinations with many other natural productions.

They are both probably diminished in immense quantities by uniting with the inflammable air [hydrogen], which arises from the mud of rivers and lakes at some seasons, when the atmosphere is light; the oxygene of the air producing water, and the azote producing volatile alkali by their combinations with this inflammable air. At other seasons of the year these principles may again change their combinations, and the atmospheric air be reproduced.[1]

And again:

(b) In the atmosphere inflammable air is probably perpetually uniting with vital air and producing moisture which descends in dews and showers, while the growth of vegetables by the assistance of light is perpetually again decomposing the water they imbibe from the earth, and while they retain the inflammable air for the formation of oils, wax, honey, resin, etc., they give up the vital air to replenish the atmosphere.[2]

It is this last note which more particularly bears upon the "blossoms," the "dying odors," and "the spherèd dew" of Shelley's lines. Shelley's metaphorical statements of scientific facts afford few instances to surpass this in indirection and beauty of figure.

[1] *Botanic Garden,* Additional Note XXXIII.
[2] *Ibid.,* note to line 204, Canto III.

The preceding instance asked for its interpretation an analogous passage in Darwin. That which follows needs nothing more than that its scientific parallel be placed beside it. Shelley's meaning is then apparent at once. In this passage Shelley has been recounting the prehistoric ages of the earth and the deluge which was supposed to have destroyed the forms of life then existing. It may be remarked, incidentally, that scientists who placed little reliance upon Biblical legend were nevertheless inclined to accept the deluge as a fact and to attribute to it the destruction of life-forms known once to exist. These are the essential lines:

> . . . and over these
> The jagged alligator, and the might
> Of earth-convulsing behemoth, which once
> Were monarch beasts, and on the slimy shores
> And weed-overgrown continents of earth,
> Increased and multiplied like summer worms
> On an abandoned corpse, till the blue globe
> Wrapped deluge round it like a cloke, and they
> Yelled, gasped and were abolished; *or some God,*
> *Whose throne was in a comet, passed, and cried,*
> *Be not! and like my words, they were no more.*
> *P. U.* IV. ll. 308-318.

Two brief citations from Humphry Davy make the meaning apparent and are quoted because of the possibility that Shelley derived his knowledge from them, though it is likely enough that he had encountered the same theory in other readings.

(a) Besides the Plutonic hypothesis, which considers rocks as the result of an existing order, and the Neptunian, which regards them as products of a slow process of creation and deposition from a chaotic fluid, there are other views in which the present state of things is supposed to have resulted from a great and extraordinary series of events, by which the ocean was carried over the land, and the secondary rocks deposited upon the primary ones. Leibnitz and Whiston refer this great revolution to the agency of a comet, by which the tides were raised above the mountains, and carried round the earth, and by which the water was heated so as to gain new solvent powers.[3]

(b) We perceive the effects of this great catastrophe [the deluge], but the immediate material cause of it can never be distinctly developed. The hypothesis of Leibnitz, extended by Whiston, that it was produced by the attraction of a comet upon the waters of the ocean, is, perhaps, the most plausible that has been advanced; and when taken with limitation, the most adequate.[4]

The passage of which this is the conclusion is a long description of the prehistoric world and of animal forms and civilizations now extinct.

> The beams flash on
> And make appear the melancholy ruins
> Of cancelled cycles; anchors, beaks of ships;
> Planks turned to marble; quivers, helms, and spears,
> And gorgon-headed targes, and the wheels
> Of scythèd chariots, and the emblazonry
> Of trophies, standards, and armorial beasts,
> Round which death laughed, sepulchred emblems
> Of dead destruction, ruin within ruin!
> The wrecks beside of many a city vast,
> Whose population which the earth grew over
> Was mortal, but not human; see, they lie,
> Their monstrous works, and uncouth skeletons,
> Their statues, homes and fanes; prodigious shapes
> Huddled in gray annihilation, split,
> Jammed in the hard, black deep; over these
> The anatomies of unknown wingèd things,
> And fishes which were isles of living scale,
> And serpents, bony chains, twisted around
> The iron crags, or within heaps of dust
> To which the tortuous strength of their last pangs

[3] John Davy, *Memoirs of the Life of Sir Humphry Davy,* I, 190.
[4] *Ibid.,* 247.

Had crushed the iron crags; over these
The jaggèd alligator, and the might
Of earth-convulsing behemoth, which once
Were monarch beasts, and on the slimy shores,
And weed-overgrown continents of earth,
Increased and multiplied like summer worms
On an abandoned corpse, till the blue globe
Wrapped deluge round it like a cloke, and they
Yelled, gasped, and were abolished;

P. U. IV. ll. 287-316.

Shelley must have derived his facts for such a passage from works on fossils, relics of ancient civilizations, etc. In a letter to Miss Hitchener of Dec. 26, 1811 Shelley writes, "I never heard of Parkinson. . . . I shall send for the 'Organic Remains.' " And in a letter of Feb. 14, 1812 to the same correspondent he writes "I have that [book] on the Organic Remains to read with you." Parkinson[5] is pretty clearly the inspiration of a number of details in Shelley's description though supplemented in all likelihood by articles in scientific journals or by other books. Mr. C. A. Brown has called attention to a number of close parallels to Shelley's lines, and these I cite from his article.[6]

In the first of the two excerpts which follow, the resemblance is general. The passage from Parkinson stresses the conversion of animal life into stone, an idea which does not appear in Shelley, who describes cities vast "whose population . . . the earth grew over." Both, however, depict vanished civilizations. The second excerpt, however, seems with its "whole ship, with its anchor" to be the likely source of Shelley's phrase "anchors, beaks of ships."

[5] James Parkinson, *Organic Remains,* Vol. I, 1804; Vol. II, 1808; Vol. III, 1811. (London).

[6] C. A. Brown, "Notes for *Prometheus Unbound." Philological Quarterly,* Vol. VII, No. 2, p. 195.

Relate to him that Valchius, in his commentary on the Klein Baur, tells of a truly curious fossil man found at Maria Kirch, near Strasburgh, by a miner who, breaking open the hollow of a rock, was astonished at beholding the figure of a man of silver, of five hundred pounds weight. If his interest and astonishment be not hereby sufficiently excited, tell him, we have more tales of wonder in store; of flocks of cattle, of large companies of men, and of even whole cities, with their inhabitants, being converted to stone. I could supply him, from a comparatively modern author, with an account of a troup of Spanish horsemen, who thus underwent the process of petrifaction.[7]

The second excerpt, besides its detail of the ship, seems expressly to justify Shelley's expression "which the earth grew over."

Tell him, I hope his faith will be comprehensive enough to enable him to receive, with full credit, the accounts delivered by Baptista Fulgosus, Lodovicus Moscardus, and Theodoris Moretus, that a whole ship, with its anchor, broken masts, and forty mariners, with their merchandise, were found, in the year 1460, in a mine fifty fathoms deep, in the neighborhood of Berne, in Switzerland.[8]

For the "planks turned to marble" of Shelley's phrase the following brief passage from Parkinson seems to be the source:

Mr. Brand informs us, that Sir Joseph Banks, Bart. and President of the Royal Society favored him with an inspection of a large specimen of fossil coal. . . . Some of them are more, and some less woody; one is a fair plank of wood.[9]

And for the alligator and behemoth of Shelley's picture the following are likely originals:

Captain William Chapman, in the fiftieth volume of the Philosophical Transactions, p. 688, gives an account of finding, on the sea shore, about half a mile from Whitby, part of the bones

---

[7] *Organic Remains*, I, 38.   [8] *Ibid*.   [9] *Ibid*., I, 121.

of an animal appearing to have been an alligator. They were found in a kind of black slate.[10]

Other animals you will find thus astonishingly entombed, possessing, indeed, many of the anatomical characteristics of animals now existing, but differing so much, in other respects, as to require to be considered, as entirely different from any which are now known to exist. Thus you will behold the bones of an animal, of which the magnitude is so great as to warrant the conviction, that the bulk of this dreadful, unknown animal, exceeded three times that of the lion; and to authorize the belief, that animals have existed, which have possessed, with all the dreadful propensities of that animal, its power of destroying, in a three-fold degree. You will also view the remains of a being of the magnitude, at least, of the elephant; which was armed with tusks, equally dreadful, as a weapon, with those borne by that animal; possessing, in addition to these, enormously huge grinders, supposed to bear the distinctive marks of those creatures, which gain their food, by preying on those of inferior powers and size. The jaws of an animal bearing a near resemblance to those of a crocodile, you will perceive to be armed with teeth, not widely different from those of the shark. In a word, you will be repeatedly astonished by the discovery of the remains of animals, of which no living prototype is to be found.[11]

There is much in Parkinson about the remains of prehistoric animals, and in the *Philosophical Transactions* of the latter years of the eighteenth and early years of the nineteenth century are numerous papers upon fossil fishes, relics of the mastodon, and human skeletons of unusual size. Shelley could not have missed these evidences of conditions of animal life different from those we know.[12] That his conception was an evolutionary one in harmony with the views of Erasmus Darwin is I believe clear from the lines:

[10] *Ibid.*, III, 281.
[11] *Ibid.*, I, 10-11.
[12] See also note to *Queen Mab* cited on p. 25.

> The wrecks beside of many a city vast,
> Whose population which the earth grew over
> Was mortal, but not human.

Precisely what his notion was of creatures capable of building cities but not human I do not know. I have found no source for this, though the superior tribe of monkeys of Helvetius' surmise may have given him the suggestion.

It was clear from our study of Darwin that vast periods of time must be postulated to account for the evolution of plant and animal forms from the "microscopic ens." Much of the scientific writing of the day assumes this vast and indeterminate history and in some of the more religiously orthodox writers attempts are made to reconcile this assumption with the Biblical account of creation. The old idea of a metaphorical implication in the book of Genesis is revived and attempts are made to interpret the six days of creation as six geologic eras. Shelley in one place seems to suggest a million years as the age of the earth.

> First Voice: *from the Mountains*
> Thrice three hundred thousand years
> O'er the earthquake's couch we stood.
>
> P. U. I. ll. 74-5.

I know of no source for so specific a guess, though in the copious scientific literature of Shelley's day one may well exist.[13]

The discovery of new elements and improved methods of analysis whereby the constituents of all matter, organic and inorganic, were shown to be the same, served in Shelley's time to emphasize the unity of the universe. A considerable but limited number of "elements" were known to be the units from which, in various combinations, every substance was created. Even the matter from outer space was composed of

---

[13] Darwin, however, surmises "millions of ages." See p. 64.

the same elements as that of our earth. Shelley expresses this idea in the following lines.

> Ye elemental Genii, who have homes
> From man's high mind even to the central stone
> Of sullen lead; from Heaven's star-fretted domes
> To the dull weed some sea-worm battens on:
>
> P. U. IV. ll. 539-542.

Two excerpts from Davy's *Chemical Philosophy* provide sufficient scientific backing for Shelley's statement.

(a) The forms and appearances of the beings and substances of the external world are almost infinitely various, and they are in a state of continued alteration: the whole surface of the earth even undergoes modifications; acted on by moisture and air, it affords the food of plants; an immense number of vegetable productions arise from apparently the same materials; these become the substance of animals; one species of animal matter is converted into another; the most perfect and beautiful of the forms of organized life ultimately decay, and are resolved into inorganic aggregates; and the same elementary substances, differently arranged, are contained in the inert soil, or bloom and emit fragrance in the flower, or become in animals the active organs of mind and intelligence.[14]

(b) As far as our investigations have extended, the same elements belong to the same parts of the system. The composition of the atmosphere and the ocean are analogous, as far as the heights of one, and the depths of the other have been examined. The matters thrown out by volcanoes are earthy or stony aggregates, and they may owe their origin to the action of air and water upon the metallic bases of the earths and alkalies; an action which may be supposed to be connected with the production of subterraneous fires. Even the substances that fall from meteors, though differing in their form and appearance from any of the bodies belonging to our earth, yet contain well known elements, silica, magnesia, sulphur, and the two magnetic metals, iron and nickel.

[14] *Elements of Chemical Philosophy*, 63.

A few undecompounded bodies, which may perhaps ultimately be resolved into still fewer elements, or which may be different forms of the same material, constitute the whole of our tangible universe of things. By experiment they are discovered, even in the most complicated arrangements; and experiment is as it were the chain that binds down the Proteus of nature, and obliges it to confess its real form and divine origin.[15]

Mr. C. A. Brown, whose parallels drawn from Parkinson were previously noted, offers a happy suggestion to elucidate the line

> To the dull weed some sea-worm battens on.

This, he believes, must allude to iodine, an element whose discovery was made known in England by Davy in a paper read on January 20, 1814 entitled "Some Experiments and Observations on a new Substance which becomes a violet-coloured gas by Heat." Davy said in part:

The discovery now announced to the Society was made about two years since by M. Courtois, a manufacturer of salt petre at Paris. It is produced from the ashes of sea-weeds. . . . The colour of its vapor has occasioned the French chemist to give it the name of iode.[16]

That Mr. Brown is correct in his surmise seems to me almost certain. He cites a number of allusions to iodine in the scientific publications of the time.[17]

Several interesting passages of mixed geological and chemical import derive from Shelley's visit to Vesuvius and its vicinity in December of 1818. His impressions are traceable in the fourth act of *Prometheus*. Especially he seems to have been struck by the evidences of wanton destruction, of some-

---

[15] *Elements of Chemical Philosophy*, 502.

[16] *Abstracts of the Papers printed in the Philosophical Transactions of the Royal Society of London*, I, 483. (1800-1814).

[17] C. A. Brown in the *Philological Quarterly*, VIII, 195-198. (April 1928).

thing malign, in the forces of nature. He remarks that "fiery stones are rained down from its darkness [the black bituminous vapor from Vesuvius] and a black shower of ashes fell even where we sat."[18] The "springs of lava" are likewise remarked.[19] And in a letter to Peacock two months later, also from Naples, is a description of his visit to the Grotta del Cane.[20]

The Grotta del Cane, too, we saw, because other people see it; but would not allow the dogs to be exhibited in torture for our curiosity. The poor little animals stood moving their tails in a slow and dismal manner, as if perfectly resigned to their condition —a cur-like emblem of voluntary servitude. The effect of the vapour, which extinguishes a torch, is to cause suffocation at last, through a process which makes the lungs feel as if they were torn by sharp points within. So a surgeon told us, who tried the experiment on himself.

First as to the "fiery stones." In *Prometheus* the Earth is rejoicing at her liberation from Jupiter:

> Sceptred curse,
> Who all our green and azure universe
> Threatenedst to muffle round with black destruction, sending
> A solid cloud to rain hot-thunder stones
> And splinter and knead down my children's bones,
> All I bring forth, to one void mass battering and blending.
> *P. U.* IV. ll. 338-443.

The obvious interpretation is that the stones are the pumice stones of a volcanic eruption. These stones, were, however, known to fall at great distances from any active volcano and speculation was various as to their origin. Cavallo in his work *The Elements of Natural and Experimental Philosophy* gives a history of the phenomenon in modern times and theories advanced to account for it.

[18] Shelley to Peacock, Dec. 22, 1818.　　[20] Feb. 25, 1819.
[19] *Ibid.*

Instances of falling stones as far back as the year 1510 are enumerated. In one, cited by Cardan, the stones were as heavy as 120 pounds, were mostly of an iron color, hard, and smelled of brimstone. Halley cites a fire ball which burst near Leghorn in 1676, raining fragments into the sea. In other instances the fall of stones was accompanied by thunder. The stones were ascertained to contain iron, were very hard on the surface and softer within, and seemed to have been exposed to intense heat. Besides iron they contained sulphur and vitrifiable earth. In some instances the clouds from which the stones fell were described as glowing, to be above the height of ordinary clouds, and to be accompanied by electrical phenomena.

The sulphureous character of the cloud and of the stones and the attendant manifestation of electrical phenomena are the points common to the various observations. The explanation cited from a Mr. King by Cavallo seems most in accord with Shelley's employment of the phenomenon and also with Beccaria's surmise as to its electrical character:

It is also well known, that a mixture of pyrites of almost any kind, beaten small, and mixed with iron filings and water, when buried in the ground, will take fire, and produce a sort of artificial volcano; and surely then, wherever a vast quantity of such kind of matter should at any time become mixed together, as flying dust or ashes, and be by any means condensed together, or compressed, the same effect might be produced, even in the atmosphere and air.

Instead, therefore, of having recourse to the supposition of the cloud in Tuscany having been produced by any other kind of exhalations from the earth, we may venture to believe, that an immense cloud of ashes, mixed with pyritical dust, and with numerous particles of iron, having been projected from Vesuvius to a most prodigious height, became afterwards condensed in its descent, took fire, both of itself as well as by means of the electric fluid it contained, produced many explosions, melted the pyritical, metallic, and argillaceous particles, of which the ashes were com-

posed; and by this means had a sudden crystallization and consolidation of those particles taken place which formed the stones of
various sizes. . . .[21]

It is Jupiter's lightning, then, which is one, if not the
sole, agency in the creation of these stones from volcanic dust.
The Earth's ascription of them to Jupiter's malevolence is,
therefore, congruous with the scientific facts and is another
instance of Shelley's symbolical association of electrical power
both with love and with hate. Throughout the poem, electrical
power in the round of nature as personified in Asia and the
Spirit of the Earth is beneficent and identifiable with love.
But power stolen from nature by Jupiter and expressed in
violence, as in lightning and its creature, the thunderstone, is
synonymous with hate. In the final overthrow of Jupiter the
Spirit of Earth returns happily to its mother Asia who now
"may cherish" it "unenvied," and the "tyrant quelling myrtle"
symbolizes the conquest of malevolent force. Of liberated man
it is said

> The lightning is his slave.

The mephitic vapors issuing from the earth under the
despotism of Jupiter are several times mentioned. The Earth,
in describing the evil which befell mankind when Prometheus
was chained with the tyrant's thunder, enumerates earth-
quake, inundation, lightning, plague, and famine and adds

> . . . and black blight on herb and tree;
> And in the corn, and vines, and meadow-grass,
> Teemed ineradicable poisonous weeds
> Draining their growth, for my wan breast was dry
> With grief, and the thin air, my breath, was stained
> With the contagion of a mother's hate
> Breathed on her child's destroyer. . . .
>
> P. U. I. ll. 173-178.

---

[21] Cavallo, IV, 391.

Again, at the portal of the chasm which leads to the realm of
Demogorgon, Asia says to Panthea

> Look, sister, ere the vapor dim thy brain:
>
> *P. U.* II. 3. l. 18.

And the chasm she thus describes:

> . . . the mighty portal,
> Like a volcano's meteor-breathing chasm,
> Whence the oracular vapor is hurled up
> Which lonely men drink wondering in their youth,
> And call truth, virtue, love, genius, or joy,
> The maddening wine of life, whose dregs they drain
> To deep intoxication; and uplift,
> Like Maenads who cry loud, Evoe! Evoe!
> The voice which is contagion to the world.
>
> *P. U.* II. 3. ll. 2-10.

Ancient writers, Plutarch and Lucan, attest the inebriating
effect of the vapors given off at the shrines of the oracles.
The priestesses, after inhaling the gas, were inspired to
prophecy. Frequently death was the consequence, for in their
enthusiasm those who had imbibed the gas sometimes hurled
themselves into the cavern.[22]   Shelley's "oracular vapor" is
seemingly likened in its effects to the enthusiasms of lonely
dreamers, whose contagious passions for truth, virtue, etc., in-
fect the world.

But what is the gas which has this effect? The mephitic
gas given off in the Grotta del Cane and in similar caverns
in volcanic districts is carbon dioxide, carbonic acid gas, a
constituent of springs and chalybeate waters. It kills, when
inhaled in quantity, not through any inherent poison but
through depriving the lungs of needed oxygen. That it was
one of the gases which emanated at the shrine of Delphi may
be premised from the tradition that it extinguished torches

---

[22] See Rees's *Cyclopedia,* article on Delphi.

thrust into it. But other of its alleged effects are not in conformity with this supposition:

That [an exhalation which issues out of a cave] of Delphi lighted those torches that were within a certain distance of it, and extinguished those which were thrust into it.[23]

That torches could be lighted at a distance from it would seem to argue the presence of another gas than carbon dioxide. Several gases, I surmise, might be the constituents of the oracular vapor and diverse effects thus be noted. Davy in his experiments had demonstrated the close association of carbonic acid with nitrous gas. I cite a passage:

These experiments are sufficient to shew that the decomposition of nitre by charcoal is a very complex process. . . . The products instead of being simply carbonic acid and nitrogen, are carbonic acid, nitrogen, nitrous acid, probably ammonia, and sometimes nitrous gas. The nitrous acid is disengaged from the base by intense heat.[24]

In another passage, again, the necessity of heat to the production of nitrous oxide is stressed:

During the solution of vegetable matters in nitric acid, by heat, very minute portions of nitrous oxide are sometimes produced, always however mingled with large quantities of nitrous gas, and carbonic acid.[25]

Of the free production of nitrous oxide in nature Davy remarks:

There are no reasons for supposing that nitrous oxide is formed in any of the processes of nature.[26]

Of the exhilarating effects and beneficent action of nitrous oxide there is copious evidence in the literature of the early

[23] Article on Oracles, *Conjuror's Magazine*, Dec. 1792, p. 169.
[24] Davy, *Collected Works*, III, 32.
[25] *Ibid.*, 132.
[26] *Ibid.*, 138.

nineteenth century. Imbibing the gas was a popular diversion and in Davy's works are records of the sensations experienced by a number of experimenters. Davy's own reactions I have previously quoted.[27] Its effects on him were similar to those of the later ether experience as remarked by William James and others. Nitrous oxide also proved its value as an anesthetic, for which purpose it is still used.

The point of all this discussion is that Shelley, well read in the science of his time and aware of the great importance attached to the new gases being discovered, especially to nitrous gas, nitrous oxide, and carbonic acid gas, and the curative effects which were hoped for from these gases in the treatment of disease, could not but be struck by the close association in nature of powers which work to man's benefit and to his destruction.[28]

We have seen how close was the association of good and evil in the instance of electricity, essential to the round of natural processes and the growth of vegetation in its atmospheric activities, and in lightning and the "thunder stone" an agent of destruction. Gases likewise were some beneficent, some maleficent in their effects on living forms, and an increase of heat or energy might transform those which are bad into those which are good.

Upon the overthrow of Jupiter the Earth is transformed:

> I hear, I feel;
> Thy lips are on me, and thy touch runs down
> Even to the adamantine central gloom

[27] See p. 107.

[28] For the use of gases in the treatment of disease see, among many: Darwin, *Zoonomia*, II, 288-9 (2 ed. 1796); *Ibid.*, 268; Davy, *Collected Works* III, 329; Priestley, *Experiments and Observations in Natural Philosophy*, I, 461-4; Cavallo, *Treatise on Air*, 636. With the exception of Davy, whose discussion has to do with the use of nitrous oxide as an anesthetic, all these references are upon the use of "fixed air," carbonic acid gas, in the treatment of disease.

Along these marble nerves, 'tis life, 'tis joy,
And, through my withered, old, and icy frame
The warmth of an immortal youth shoots down
Circling. Henceforth the many children fair
Folded in my sustaining arms; all plants,
And creeping forms, and insects rainbow-winged,
And birds, and beasts, and fish, and human shapes,
Which drew disease and pain from my wan bosom,
Draining the poison of despair, shall take
And interchange sweet nutriment;

. . . .
                    night-folded flowers
Shall suck unwithering hues in their repose;
                    P. U. III. 3. ll. 84-102.

It is life, love, energy, heat which "interpenetrates" the earth's
"granite mass" and changes the character of the vapors which
she emits.

                    . . . there is a cavern where my spirit
Was panted forth in anguish whilst thy pain
Made my heart mad, and those who did inhale it
Became mad too, and built a temple there,
And spoke, and were oracular, and lured
The erring nations round to mutual war,
And faithless faith, such as Jove kept with thee;
Which breath now rises as amongst tall weeds
A violet's exhalation, and it fills
With a serener light and crimson air
Intense, yet soft, the rocks and woods around;
It feeds the quick growth of the serpent vine,
And the dark linkèd ivy. . . .
                    P. U. III. 3. ll. 124-136.

It is the phrase "crimson air" which identifies the earth's
exhalation as nitrous gas. The color is remarked by Priestley,
Davy, and all other experimenters when nitrous gas is mixed
with air, and to no other gas commonly discussed in this day
does the description apply:

On mingling a little of it with atmospheric air, it gave a red vapour . . . it was nitrous gas nearly pure.[29]

And again, from Priestley:

One of the most conspicuous properties of this kind of air [nitrous air] is the great diminution of any quantity of common air, with which it is mixed, attended with a turbid red, or deep orange colour, and a considerable heat.[30]

Further confirmation is to be found in Darwin's lines descriptive of the same phenomenon. Azotic gas is nitrogen. The passage describes the chemical union of nitrogen and oxygen:

> As woos Azotic Gas the virgin Air,
> And veils in *crimson clouds* the yielding Fair,
> Indignant fire the treacherous courtship flies,
> Waves his light wing, and mingles with the skies.
> *Botanic Garden,* II. ll. 147-150.

That the earth newly animated and generating greater heat could transform mephitic gases to such as are beneficent in their effects, may be a not too fanciful extension of Davy's conclusion, previously noted, that nitrous oxide and nitrous gas are produced from nitric acid upon the application of heat. I am not sufficient of a chemist to determine whether or no Shelley sacrifices his scientific to his poetic character in this instance; whether his extension of Davy's conclusion is beyond scientific plausibility. I can, in any case, see no other meaning for "crimson air" than nitrous gas. The word "air" was commonly used at the beginning of the nineteenth century in the sense of "gas." And "crimson" can justly be used only of nitrous gas.

[29] Davy, *Collected Works,* III, 99.
[30] Joseph Priestley, *Experiments and Observations on Different Kinds of Air,* I, 110 (3 ed. 1781).

That the nitrous gas would "feed the quick growth of the serpent vine" does not, however, appear with any certainty from the experiments recorded by Priestley and Davy upon the effect of nitrous gas on plant growth. Because nitrogen is so important a constituent of plants it was evidently assumed that a gas rich in nitrogen would stimulate their growth. The results, both in the instance of Davy and Priestley, are inconclusive.[31] It may very well be, however, that Shelley's justification for his use of this supposed fact lies in the report of some experiment which I have not encountered. A similar instance, it will be recalled, had to do with the effects of electricity upon plant growth; the findings of experimenters were at variance. Shelley followed Darwin in attributing to electrical action a quickening effect.

Associated with healing gases are medicinal springs, of which Darwin in the *Botanic Garden* has a good deal to say. One passage in the fourth act of *Prometheus* ascribes to such a spring of volcanic origin great powers of healing:

> Leave Man even as a leprous child is left,
> Who follows a sick beast to some warm cleft
> Of rocks, through which the might of healing
>   springs is poured;
> Then when it wanders home with rosy smile,
> Unconscious, and its mother fears awhile
> It is a spirit, then weeps on her child restored;
>
> P. U. IV. ll. 388-393.

"Leprous" I suppose to mean not literally infected with leprosy but with some skin disease. Rees's *Cyclopedia* ascribes to Malvern springs in Worcestershire these powers:

Malvern water is used both externally and internally. Externally applied, it is stated to be a most useful application to deep seated ulcerations of a scrofulous nature, and to various cutaneous affections.[32]

[31] See Appendix I to vol. III of Davy's *Collected Works*.
[32] Rees's *Cyclopedia*, article on Water.

Shelley may have had in mind some instance from his read-ing, ancient or modern; the reference to the "sick beast" makes me think that to be the case. But I have not identified it.

There are a number of other allusions in *Prometheus* which, though obviously scientific, have not fallen under the head of previous classifications. Thus the Earth speaks of "my granite mass," "my cloven fire-crags," and "adamantine central gloom." These lead me to believe that Shelley subscribed to the theory of a granite core of the earth with pockets or wells of volcanic fire rather than to the theory that the center of the earth was molten. In the geological theory of the time both specula-tions were advanced.

In the following passage stalactites are meant:

> From its curved roof the mountain's frozen tears,
> Like snow, or silver, or long diamond spires,
> Hang downward. . . .
>
> *P. U.* III. 3. ll. 15-17.

It is a characteristic example of Shelley's power of phrasing an exact scientific fact in poetic imagery.

What is the allusion in the next instance does not so clearly appear:

> And caverns in crystalline columns poised
> With vegetable silver overspread;
>
> *P. U.* IV. ll. 282-3.

"Vegetable silver" is not, so far as I can discover, a scientific term. Shelley means apparently some floriate mineral pattern silvery in color. There are several passages in Darwin which may have suggested Shelley's phrase:

> Hence orient Nitre owes its sparkling birth,
> And with prismatic crystals gems the earth,
> O'er tottering domes in filmy foliage crawls,
> Or frosts with branching plumes the mouldering walls.
>
> *Botanic Garden*, II. ll. 143-146.

Again in a note on nitre he speaks of the "efflorescence of various beautiful leafy and hairy forms." There was also a familiar chemical experiment which Shelley may have himself performed, that known as Diana's Trees. It is thus described in Darwin:

> So the learn'd Alchemist exulting sees
> Rise in his bright mattrass Diana's trees;
> Drop after drop, with just delay he pours
> The red-fumed acid on Potosi's ores;
> With sudden flash the fierce bullitions rise,
> And wide in air the gas phlogistic flies;
> Slow shoot, at length, in many a brilliant mass
> Metallic roots across the netted glass.
> Branch after branch extend their silver stems,
> Bud into gold, and blossom into gems.
>
> *Botanic Garden,* IV. ll. 581-590.

The experiment is performed by dissolving silver in nitric acid to which distilled water and mercury are added. Hogg's horrified discovery of the tea-cup in which a silver coin was dissolving in acid may have interrupted this particular experiment.[33]

Some of the allusions in *Prometheus* are, if scientific, clearly speculative and not on the order of the science I have previously discussed. Thus the Echoes of Act II are not echoes properly at all:

> Echoes we: listen
> We cannot stay:
> As dew-stars glisten
> Then fade away—
> Child of Ocean!
>
> *P. U.* II. 1. ll. 166-170.

Echoes with such individual powers are reminiscent of Bacon's description of strange inventions in the *New Atlantis:*

[33] See p. 10.

We have also divers strange and artificial echoes, reflecting the voice many times, and as it were tossing it; and some that give back the voice louder than it came, some shriller and some deeper; yea some rendering the voice, differing in the letters or articulate sound from that they receive.[34]

Again, an instance of the supposed pre-natal influence of art objects is pseudo-scientific or legendary in its authority, though Darwin, it will be recalled, had theories concerning the father's power, through the imagination, of determining the character of offspring.

> Through the cold mass
> Of marble and of color his dreams pass—
> Bright threads whence mothers weave the robes
> their children wear.
>
> *P. U.* IV. ll. 412-414.

A classical, though extreme, instance of this ancient belief may be cited from the Greek romance, *Aethiopica, or Theagenes and Chariclea:*

The daughter of Hydaspes and Persina, King and Queen of Ethiopia, was born white, her mother at the moment of conception having gazed intently upon a painting of white Andromeda.[35]

This instance is clearly on the utmost verge of science, if not beyond it, and with it I shall bring the annotation of specific passages to a close. I have, it is likely, overlooked some lines of scientific import and of those I have endeavored to interpret some, it is even more probable, I have misread. Yet there are many others whose scientific interpretation has been so clear in terms of the citations brought to bear upon them that I feel the general thesis of this book has been sustained and the pervasive character of Shelley's scientific thought in *Prometheus* established. That this scientific reading has made clear large parts of the poem previously unintelligible is evident.

[34] *New Atlantis,* 209.
[35] Wolff, *The Greek Romances in Elizabethan Prose Fiction,* 11.

CHAPTER XII

CONCLUSION

THE PROMETHEAN AGE of Shelley's vision is one in which mankind has cast out hate and fear, has destroyed the evil deity of its own creation, and through its mastery of science controls the forces of nature:

> The lightning is his slave; heaven's utmost deep
> Gives up her stars, and like a flock of sheep
> They pass before his eyes, are numbered, and roll on!
> The tempest is his steed, he strides the air;
> And the abyss shouts from her depth laid bare,
> 'Heaven, hast thou secrets? Man unveils me: I have none'!
>
> *P. U.* IV. ll. 418-423.

Shelley's belief that man's physical perfection was to be coincident with his moral regeneration and that all nature, animate and inanimate, would share in his liberation from pain and sin was expressed in *Queen Mab*. Therein an evolutionary process in the attainment of this goal was clearly stated. In *Prometheus* the evolutionary emphasis is not so explicit. The Titan, it is true, attains his freedom and happiness through his own inner change and is the creator of his own destiny, a conception which is in harmony with Erasmus Darwin's belief that changes in plant and animal are volitional, are from within out, and not, as in the later theory of evolution, determined by the pressure of environment. For dramatic effectiveness, in *Prometheus* the conflict of man with his own evil nature and with his environment is externalized. Jupiter is the adversary in the struggle whose climactic moments are the theme of the drama. The change, therefore, in the Titan's soul and the resultant change in all nature is catastrophic, dramatically much more effective than the story of a slow evolution but false to fact. Shelley, in short, is speaking in the form of a parable.

To the theme of man's moral regeneration and the consequent transformation of the physical universe common to *Queen Mab* and *Prometheus,* Shelley in the latter poem adds the thought of man's mastery through science of the forces of nature.

Heaven, hast thou secrets? Man unveils me; I have none.

It is to be noted that this mastery comes only as mankind ceases to be a group of warring individuals and shares a common mind and soul. Shelley thus expresses his thought:

> Man, oh, not men! a chain of linkèd thought,
> Of love and might to be divided not,
> Compelling the elements with adamantine stress;
> . . . .
> Man, one harmonious soul of many a soul,
> Whose nature is its own divine control.
>
> P. U. IV. ll. 394-401.

Shelley seems to express here his belief in the unity of knowledge, his belief that the individual adds his bit to the whole, is a drop in the ocean of mind, but of himself is nothing. The thought is Platonistic, or expresses as intelligibly as words can convey it, the Indian idea of Nirvana. Science, knowledge, in which all share and to which all contribute, is, like love, a way to the loss of the individual self in the attainment of the larger self. So Shelley seems to imply, with, it may be, prophetic insight. For the Utopia of which he dreamed will come, if ever, only as good-will among mankind and intellectual inter-dependence unite them. Complete realization of the latter may create the former. Science may necessitate the federation of the world.

I am tempted to expatiate upon what is sufficiently obvious, the prophetic character of Shelley's thought in science, its anticipations of modern beliefs and theories. But Shelley is not alone in this and, as the pages of this book have shown, his ideas derive from many sources. He truly is but one link in the "chain of linkèd thought." It is of the nature of philosophic thought to anticipate what is to come, often only after centuries. The speculations of the Greeks that hit so closely the truths of natural history are verified in our time. The Prometheus myth itself allegorizes man's conflict with the forces of nature and predicts his mastery of them. Shelley's greatness lies in his power to discern *relationships among diverse ideas, to synthesize them, and to express them in memorable and beautiful form. His form in *Prometheus Unbound* is difficult and recondite partly because the ideas are complex and difficult and partly because he was heedless of an audience. His indifference to his readers is a defect but explicable; and once *Prometheus Unbound* is understood it will repay with the richness of its revelation the toil required of it.

The importance that attaches to *Prometheus Unbound* is, in my belief, as much philosophic as poetic. That Shelley's scientific conception of the universe was very much like our own has this significance chiefly; the problem which he sought to solve is, in its terms, the problem which we have set ourselves: to reconcile materialistic with mystical thought or, as we inadequately phrase it, "science and religion." Shelley will be, as a thinker, valued by the modern world to the degree in which his statement of the problem is like our own and his solution of it satisfying. Once understood his statement of it is, indeed, very much like ours. Whether his solution will generally commend itself remains to be seen. My own belief is that *Prometheus Unbound* is not only a beautiful poem but necessarily, if beautiful, filled with stimulating and profound ideas. I think it one of the few great philosophical poems in English.

In this book only one strand of Shelley's thought has been unravelled. The Platonistic strand is more difficult because the conclusions at which the interpreter arrives are necessarily more difficult to substantiate, are less demonstrably based on particular books. In many passages of scientific import it was necessary only to cite prose parallels to make the meaning obvious. But the solution of the scientific metaphors is a certain augury of the solution of the more difficult Platonistic passages, for it makes clear first, that some meaning underlies lines which seem superficially only fanciful; and, second and chief, it shows sufficient of Shelley's mind to premise that his metaphysical implications will be consistent with, harmonious with, his scientific beliefs. Shelley is a recondite thinker with a poet's gift of expressing an intellectual idea in metaphor of sense impressions. He is bilingual. Yet being, as he is, fundamentally intellectual, his philosophy is unified and consistent. It can, therefore, be analyzed and grasped.

Shelley's unusual power of expressing intellectual and abstract ideas in terms of sense has been illustrated throughout the discussion of *Prometheus*. I wish, however, to cite two simple instances, not before discussed, to emphasize this faculty, for obvious as it is upon reflection, it seems generally not to be perceived even by lovers of his verse.

> The crawling glaciers pierce me with their spears.
> *P. U.* I. l. 31.

The fact that glaciers crawl is not visually perceived. It is a scientific fact intellectually grasped and translated into a visual image. Another instance:

'Tis the deep music of the rolling world,
Kindling within the strings of the waved air
Aeolian modulations.

P. U. IV. ll. 186-188.

Here the expression "waved air" is the expression of a scientific fact. It is not one grasped by the senses.

Shelley remarked in a letter to Peacock, "You know I always seek in what I see the manifestation of something beyond the present and tangible object."[1] This is only half expressive of his peculiar poetic power. Not only does he look beneath the surface of impressions to understand their meaning, but meanings intellectually perceived he seeks to set forth in sensible images, to externalize. Shelley was not, when he first wrote poetry, notably an observer of sense impressions. Compare him with Keats and realize their profound difference. He lived almost wholly in the intellect and the sympathetic emotions. As he matures his work gains in concreteness. Partly he sought relief in his later years from the melancholy of his own frustrated thought. The external world provided some consolation. He began to observe. The range of his sense impressions, as recorded in his verse, widens. A nature too intellectual, too philosophical, an imagination too sensitive to the sufferings of man found relief in the selfless observation of nature. In a sense, despite his sympathy and charity, Shelley was self-centered and egotistical. But he became less so as he matured. The *Cenci* is evidence of his power to get out of himself. It is proof that his poetic range was potentially that of the greatest poets. He did not wholly realize his possibilities.

The processes of Shelley's creative imagination have to some degree been suggested in the preceding chapters. To trace these processes as Professor Lowes has done for Cole-

[1] Nov. 6, 1818.

ridge has not been my particular task. I have sought only
to elucidate Shelley's meaning. In so doing, the work of
Erasmus Darwin has been an invaluable instrument. It is
evident that at some time Darwin made a profound impression upon Shelley's thought and imagination. There are
more verbal echoes of Darwin in Shelley's scientific passages
than of any other scientific writer. Yet definite as are these
verbal echoes they are after all relatively few. Whereas Coleridge, as Professor Lowes demonstrates, treasured words and
phrases in his subconscious mind, Shelley remembers usually
the idea, not the phrasing of the idea. It is so, too, in his
Platonism. *Prometheus* is saturated with Platonism, but
verbal indebtedness is very hard to trace and is apparently
slight. Shelley, I conceive, was a much more intellectual man
than Coleridge. This is to reverse the critical opinion of a
hundred years but is, I believe, justified by the evidence.

There remains also, for the student of poetry, a fascinating
problem in aesthetics. Darwin, one of the worst of poets, expresses ideas which are oftentimes the same as those of Shelley,
one of the best of poets. Though both turn scientific ideas
into verse, in exploring Darwin for his content the sensitive
reader must often stop his ears; while in reading Shelley one
is forever so seduced by the beauty of form that the mind fails
to perceive within the fragile lyric its firm intellectual concept.
Yet the idea is as clear and as well articulated, once it is de-
ciphered, as is the pattern of the verse itself in its rhythms,
its echoes, its variations, and repetitions.

INDEX

ADONIS, 62.

Aethiopica, or Theagenes and Chariclea, 194.

Air and other Elastic Fluids, Treatise on, Cavallo, 125.

Ancient Mariner, The, 127.

Animation, spirit of, 57; elec. soul of universe, 95; animal heat from solar ray, 95; anal. to light, 96; derives from ether, 98; ident. w love and elec., 132-3.

Astronomy, Shelley's early interest in, 4, 6; allus. to in *Q.M.,* 14 *seq.;* Herschel, 43; moon, 45; Herschel's proofs of cosmic evol., 81 *seq.;* stellar universe, 86; volcanoes in moon, 88; phys. char. of moon, 152 *seq.;* mag. attr. of moon, 162; gravitation, 164; universe infinite, 165; earth's shadow, 167; Pliny, 168; "implicated orbits," 169; ancient knowl. of comets, 170; movement of solar system, 170.

Aurora Borealis, 53, 55; Davy's theory, 112; history, 145; color, 146; cause, 146; Beccaria's theory, 147; Davy's theory, 147; southern, 156; artific. produced, 157.

BACON, *New Atlantis,* 193.

Bailly, *Lettres sur les Sciences, à Voltaire,* 25; return of comets, 170.

Beccaria, Father Giambatista, x; work on atmos. elec., 118; source of *The Cloud,* 119; atmos. elec. in serene weather, 120; phosphor., 123; elec. terminal: "the star," 126; elec. of fogs, 127; at noon, 129; at sunrise, 130; elec. in body, 133; air resist. to elec. flash, 136; elec. explodes water, 137; theory of Aurora, 147; myrtles elec., 150; "star" and "brush," 155.

Berkeley, 41, 102.

Birch, *History of the Royal Society,* 92.

Boscovich, 114.

Botanic Garden, The. See *Darwin.*

Boyle, 92, 96.

Brown, C. A., "Notes for *Prometheus Unbound,*" 177; iodine, 182.

Brown, Thomas, 69.

Buffon, 61-2, 65; moon's motion, 162.

Burtt, *Metaphysical Foundations of Physics,* 167.

CABANIS, *Rapports du Physique et du moral de l'Homme,* 25.

Canning, 32.

Cavallo, 125, 131, 163, 168, 183, 184.

Cavendish, 53.

Cenci, The, 199.

Chemical Philosophy, Davy, 110.

Clarke, Agnes M., *The Herschels and Modern Astronomy,* 81.

Cloud, The, key to *P.U.,* 119; derived from Beccaria, 119-120; "convex gleams," 154.

Clouds, 53, 55; theory of formation, 137; symbol of fertility, 167.

Coleridge, 88, 108, 126, 199.

Comet, cause of Flood, 175.

DAEMON, 167.

Dalton, 104.

Darwin, Charles, 62.

Darwin, Erasmus, x, 3, 7, 9, 22; echoes of, in *Queen Mab,* 23; theory of climate, 26, 29; char. and impor. to Shelley, 30-31; disrepute after death, 31; *Memoirs* by Anna Seward, 31; *Loves of the Plants* parod. by Canning, 32; imit. school of Pope, 32; design of *Botanic Garden,* 33; Rosicr. myth., 33; *Rape of the Lock,* 34; infl. on S's myth., 34; poetic use of sci., 36; predicts air-plane, 36; control of winds and climate, 37; refl. field of sci., 38; dates of works, 38; theme of *The Temple of Nature,* 39; Deist, 40; love, ruler of universe, 40; concepts of matter and motion, 41; nom. accept. of immater., 42; cosmic universe, 42; destr. and recr. of univ., 44; frozen seas in moon, 45; volcanoes in